A MAP OF THE HUMAN BRAIN

THE GROSS ANATOMY OF THE HUMAN BRAIN

FUNCTIONAL HEALTH SERIES

SAM FURY

WARNINGS AND DISCLAIMERS

CONTENTS

THANKS FOR YOUR PURCHASE

Get Your Next SF Nonfiction Book FREE!

Claim the book of your choice at:

https://www.SFNonfictionBooks.com/Free-Book

You will also be among the first to know of all the latest releases, discount offers, bonus content, and more.

Go to:

https://www.SFNonfictionBooks.com/Free-Book

Thanks again for your support.

INTRODUCTION TO THE HUMAN BRAIN

The Significance of Studying the Brain

The Importance of Neuroscience

The human brain only makes up two percent of the average body weight of a 150-pound adult but is responsible for interpreting all signals from the environment and translating them into meaningful information. The brain not only controls our memory, emotion, and intelligence but also enables us to move, talk, hear, taste, smell, and sense. It also regulates the body's internal and external organs, allowing them to function effectively in response to various stimuli. Encapsulated within a protective bony structure, called the skull, the human brain is a gelatinous mass buffered by cerebrospinal fluid. It is composed of 60% fat and 40% composite of carbohydrates, proteins, fats, and salts. It forms part of the larger central nervous system (CNS), alongside the spinal cord and twelve cranial nerves that control motor skills and sensations. Made up of gray and white matter, the brain is a network of blood vessels and nerves, called neurons and glial cells.

Neuroscience is a field of study that focuses on understanding how the brain and nervous system develop and function. It not only studies the biology of the brain and nervous system but also focuses on the cellular, evolutionary, molecular, functional, and medical components. A relatively new scientific discipline, neuroscience was only formally recognized as a field of study in the 20th Century. It helps us understand how and why humans respond to their environment behaviorally, emotionally, and physically. The field of neuroscience is also critical for the understanding of a variety of common illnesses, disorders, and conditions like addiction, epilepsy, stroke, schizophrenia, and autistic spectrum disorders. Because of the complexity of the nervous system, neuroscience is regarded as a multidisciplinary study in that it includes the science of genetics, anatomy, psychology, chemistry, medicine, and philosophy.

There are several branches of neuroscience, including behavioral, clinical, cellular, developmental, and cognitive. The brain is central to the study of neuroscience as it holds the very essence of our behaviors, movements, preferences, moods, memories, personalities, and abilities. To understand the brain is to understand who we are as humans and individuals.

Impact on Understanding Human Behaviors and Cognition

The brain is divided up into several structures, each responsible for specific bodily functions like sleeping, breathing, and seeing, as well as how humans respond emotionally to situations. It is the origin of our thoughts, feelings, creativity, and perceptions of the world around us. It is a complex organized organ that governs every single process that takes place in our body.

One of the main roles of the brain is to regulate and control cognition. Defined as "the processes involved in gaining knowledge and comprehension" (Cherry, 2023, para. 1), cognitive processes manage both our conscious and unconscious perceptions, along with our thinking, knowledge acquisition, problem-solving, and reasoning. The brain allows us to receive external and internal information and process it so that we can carry out relevant tasks as a result. This is called the cognitive function of the brain and includes our ability to receive, store, select, develop, recover, and transform information appropriately (Zhang, 2019).

Various structures in the brain are responsible for regulating behavior and emotion, namely the amygdala, prefrontal cortex, anterior cingulate, ventral striatum, and insula. They take various stimuli and messages received from the external environment and process them so that the brain and body can respond accordingly. For example, the prefrontal cortex, which is found behind the forehead, can anticipate the results of our behaviors and decisions and regulate our behavior and emotions appropriately. Illness or injury to certain areas of the brain can affect the way the brain works and, consequently, how someone processes and acts on environmental messages and stimuli. Suppose we understand how the brain receives and processes various environmental stimuli. In that case, we can understand how someone may react to a certain situation and why they react the way they do, especially if a part of the brain is injured or becomes dysfunctional.

Certain neurological disorders, like dementia, Alzheimer's, or Parkinson's disease, change the way a person behaves and displays emotion. Studying the brain to learn how it is affected by these diseases and illnesses can help in understanding the sufferer's change in behavioral and emotional patterns. The study of the brain and how it affects behavior is a field of study known as bio-psychology or behavioral neuroscience. Behavioral neuroscience aims to understand the brain's structure and components and how they affect a person's mental well-being and functionality.

Historical Overview

Early Observations and Misconceptions of the Brain

Interest in the brain has a long and complex history. In Ancient Egypt, records show that the brain was considered an inconsequential organ of the body with no real significance. However, several hundred years later, classical-era scientists, researchers, and philosophers started showing an increased interest in how the brain contributes to functions in the body and mind. Doctors and physicians as far back as 2,000 years ago understood that the brain was the "seat of complex thought." Grecian-Roman physician and philosopher, Galen, who was born in 129, was instrumental in furthering the understanding of the anatomy of the brain. He believed the brain was the *hêgemonikon* or the "central command centre of the soul," the location of memory, thinking, and personality (Retief and Cilliers, 2008).

In later years, around the Middle Ages, prominent physicians and philosophers like Avicenna and de Liuzzi started suggesting that the brain processed signals received from the five senses and preserved that information as memory. Towards the end of the 15th Century, approximately 500 years ago, scientists like Leonardo da Vinci, Jacopo Berengario da Carpi, and Alessandro Achillini noted that the brain potentially housed the "soul" or "spirit." As time went on and researchers continued to perform extensive dissections of the human body, knowledge of the brain's anatomy increased substantially. By the early 17th century, the physical structure of the brain was well-described, but understanding of its function was still limited.

Technology like microscopes increased the ability of physicians to examine the brain and, by the early 1900s, a group of English and Australian biologists and physiologists recognized neurons as the mode of communication from the body to the brain. This discovery later won them a posthumous Nobel Prize.

Since the 1960s, research into the brain and its functions has increased dramatically, as has the understanding of its role in cognition and behavior. For centuries, there abounded numerous misconceptions about the brain and how it works. Aristotle believed the brain was simply the body's "radiator," dispelling heat from the heart. Galen suggested the brain was composed of sperm cells. Many philosophers believed the brain cavities or ventricles contained spinal fluid that housed the soul. Physicians argued over whether the humoral aspects of the brain were "hot," "cool," or "moist."

Milestones in Brain Research

For the past fifty years, the field of neuroscience has seen a dramatic surge as knowledge of the brain, its functions, and its effect on behavior and cognition has become clearer. Lagercrantz (2021) suggests that there are, amongst others, five key milestones in the history of neuroscience:

1. In the 17th Century, English physician, Thomas Willis, disputed early misconceptions that the brain was the heart's cooling system and that mental capacities were housed in the heart. He suggested that the brain's gray matter was the seat of higher thinking. Later, work by various philosophers

and physicians led to the development of the theory of epigenesis, whereby organisms develop from a mass of cells. This theory furthered the science of brain development.

2. In the 19th Century, celebrated neuroanatomist, Santiago Ramon y Cajal, founded modern neurobiology, receiving the Nobel Prize for Physiology in 1906. Cajal identified the neural theory, suggesting that neurons were separate cells that communicated with one another through what were later called synapses.

3. Hans Spermann, a German embryologist, won the Nobel Prize for Medicine in 1935 for his work and that of his student, Hilde Mangold (Proescholdt). Together, they believed that they had discovered how the brain was organised.

4. In the 1940s, Rita Levi-Montalcini, an Italian researcher, worked closely with German embryologist, Viktor Hamburger, on developing the nerve growth factor. This important discovery for neurobiology suggested that a protein called the nerve growth factor (NGF) is responsible for the growth and survival of nerves of the nervous system.

5. In 2006, a group of Swedish researchers, led by Jonas Frisén, discovered that, while no new neurons are produced after birth in the neocortex, new neurons can be formed in the hippocampus over time. This finding corroborated Eastern European neuroscientist, Pasko Rakic's, theory that new neurons are only formed in the hippocampus, deep within the temporal lobe.

Key Figures in Brain Anatomy and Physiology

In the early 1800s, scientists were unable to attribute the cell theory (that cells are the basic structural unit of organisms) to brain tissue, as they were unable to identify individual brain cells. Decades later, Camillo Golgi, an Italian physician, accidentally colored neurons with a chemical reaction that allowed him to identify individual neurons and their dendrites and axons.

In later years, Santiago Ramon y Cajal standardized Golgi's black reaction procedure, and in doing so was able to identify three main components of nerve cells: the cell body, the axons, and the dendrites. He also recognized that neurons communicated with one another via a nerve "signal." Based on Cajal's work, two later physicians, Heinrich Wilhelm Waldeyer and Charles Sherrington, would respectively coin the terms "neuron" and "synapse."

The work of David Hubel and Torsten Wiesel was integral to our current understanding of how the brain processes visual stimuli. They also identified the critical period within which the visual pathways are consolidated, after which they cannot change.

In more recent years, neuroscientists' ability to understand the structure and function of the brain has been elevated with the use of magnetic resonance imagery (MRI). Using radio and magnetic waves, the MRI can produce detailed images of living brains. Pioneered by Raymond Damadian in 1977, magnetic resonance scanning reveals intricate images of parts of the body. Further improved by Paul Lauterbur and Peter Mansfield, the process of MRI has since confirmed the brain's plasticity or its ability to adapt at any age. This is also called cerebral or neuroplasticity.

In our constant endeavors to treat and prevent heritable brain diseases, Professors Jennifer Doudna and Emmanuelle Charpentier pioneered the use of gene editing to alter gene expressions. Developed in 2012, this technique will hopefully enable scientists to edit various DNA in mammalian brains to treat genetic brain disorders or brain diseases like cancer.

BUILDING BLOCKS: NEURONS AND GLIA

Neurons: The Brain's Communicators

Neurons, or nerve cells, are the cells of the brain that allow signals to be communicated to and from the brain. Essentially, they can be referred to as the "building blocks" of the brain. The term "neuron" was coined by German anatomist, Heindrich Wilhelm Waldemeyer in 1891. It is based on the ancient Greek word for sinew or bowstring. Neurons use a form of electricity, called action potentials, to allow a signal to flow along the body of the neuron and into the presynaptic endings. Neurons can pass along both chemical and electrical signals. Chemical signals are communicated by neuro-transmitters, while electrical signals occur when a positive electrical signal is passed across a tiny gap between neurons called the gap junction. Neurons move messages between one another, within the brain, and between the brain, body, and spinal cord. Neurons vary greatly in size, from mere nanometers to over a meter in length.

Neuron Structure

There are three main components to the structure of a neuron, namely, the cell body, the dendrites, and the axons. The cell body is also called the soma. It contains the cell's genetic material within the nucleus. The soma is also responsible for controlling the cell's activities. It generates energy for the nerve to function and maintains the structure of the neuron. The cell body is covered by a membrane and contains a Golgi body, mitochondria, and endoplasmic reticulum.

Two branches emerge from either end of the neuron. The dendrite is an extension of the cell body that receives signals from other neurons and then transfers that information to the cell body, where it is interpreted and acted upon. Dendrites have a fibrous structure that sometimes forms a set of root-like assemblages in what is called a "dendritic tree." They also contain receptors that can receive and process neurotransmitters that are released into the synapses from other neurons.

While the dendritic structure of the neuron receives messages, the axon is a slender tube-like "tail" that moves signals away from the cell body. These impulses are then passed along axon terminals to the adjacent neuron. Axons are covered by myelin, which is a layer of insulating material that assists in conducting electrical signals along the axon body. The axon is joined to the cell body by a structure called the axon hillock.

Information is transferred between neurons through chemical signals called neurotransmitters. The terminal area of the axon releases neurotransmitters from sacs called vesicles. The neurotransmitters are then received by specialized receptors on the dendrite. The small spaces or junctions between the terminal end of the axon and the receiving ends of the dendritic tree are called synapses.

Types of Neurons

There are three main functional types of neurons: sensory, motor, and interneurons. Each type plays a function in receiving and processing specific information for different parts of the body. The sensory or afferent neurons receive and process information from the various senses. Chemical and physical stimuli from the external environment are converted into information that neurons send to the brain and spinal cord. Sensory neurons react to information received from the skin, eyes, ears, muscles, and other organs, and process inputs like pain, smell, taste, feeling, and sound. Sensory neurons usually only have a single axon and long branches on the dendrite, and an area called pseudounipolar or unipolar neurons.

Motor neurons are also referred to as efferent neurons. They are multipolar neurons, which means they generally have a single axon process but multiple dendrites from the cell body. Multipolar neurons are very common and are found in both the central and peripheral nervous systems. Motor neurons send information from the brain to various muscles, glands, and organs in the body, allowing voluntary physical movements such as talking, walking, and eating. Motor neurons that transmit signals from the brain to the spinal cord are called upper motor neurons, while those that carry information from the spinal cord and various muscles are called lower motor neurons.

Interneurons are also multipolar and, as per their name, connect sensory and motor neurons by their axons. Found in both the brain and the spinal cord, but not in the body, interneurons form information circuits that allow signals to be sent from sensory to motor neurons to allow action to be taken in response to the external environment. Interneurons are also called associative neurons.

There are two other types of neurons based on their structure and role in signal transmission. Pyramidal cells or neurons are multipolar, with one axon and several dendrites. Their cell bodies are arranged in the shape of a pyramid. They are found in the amygdala, hippocampus, and cerebral cortex. Pyramidal neurons are excitatory, which means they are stimulated to generate a signal so that it can be passed to the next cell. They are involved in cognitive processes like learning and decision-making.

Purkinje neurons are structurally unique in that they have a single dendritic tree with multiple branches that extend away from the cell body. They are inhibitory neurons in that they prevent other neurons from generating an action potential by releasing specific neurotransmitters. This inhibits or reduces activity in the next neuron in the circuit.

Action Potentials and Nerve Impulses

Signals or information are passed between the brain, spinal cord, and body through a complex network of nerve cells or neurons. Signals move from one neuron to the next through a process called an action potential. Simply put, this is when the electrical potential of a neuron's membrane is changed so that a signal can be transmitted. This change is caused by the movement of charged particles across the neuron's membrane. At rest, the electrical charge of the inside of a neuron is negative, compared to the external environment. This is called the neuron's resting potential.

Neurons are surrounded by a semi-permeable membrane, which means only selected ions (electrically charged chemicals) are allowed to pass through channels on the membrane. There are four main ions located within the nervous system, namely calcium (Ca+), which has two positive charges (++), chloride (Cl-), which has one negative charge (-), and sodium (Na+) and potassium (K+), both of which have one positive charge (+). A neuron can also contain negatively charged protein molecules. When at rest, the negatively charged protein molecules cannot move across the membrane of a neuron, while positively charged potassium ions can. This is called the neuron resting potential. At rest, there are more K+ ions inside the neuron and more Na+ ions outside the neuron. The charge of a neuron at rest is 70 millivolts (mV) lower than its surrounding environment, and the channels are closed to certain ions.

When one neuron is stimulated electrically by an adjacent neuron, an action potential occurs. This is also called a 'spike' or 'impulse' and the ion channels in the membrane open, allowing certain positively charged ions, like Na+, to pass into the cell. Stimuli can be electrical or chemical (the release of neurotransmitters). Because of the influx of positively charged ions into the cell, its potential changes and it becomes more positive than negative. This process is called depolarization.

Once enough positively charged Na+ ions have entered the cell, a threshold of polarity is reached, which is usually around -55 mV. Once this threshold is reached, certain sodium channels, called voltage-gated sodium channels, open rapidly. These channels are called voltage-gated channels because their opening is influenced by a change in the resting potential of a cell to 0mV, caused by electrical activity. The rapid opening of voltage-gated sodium channels allows many more Na+ ions to enter the cell. The critical threshold level is the same across all neurons, regardless of neuron type or stimulus strength. This means that an action potential will only fire once the threshold level is reached, which is known as the "all or nothing" principle.

As Na+ ions rush into the cell, the potential of the membrane rises, reaching 0 mV and increasing further to around +40 mV. This is called the rising phase. At this point, there are many more Na+ ions inside the cell than outside it, which makes it more positively charged than its external environment. Voltage-gated sodium channels start closing, while voltage-gated potassium channels open. This allows K+ ions to move out of the cell, once again repolarizing the cell's membrane potential to its resting state of -70 mV.

Generally, the repolarization of the cell causes the membrane potential to increase slightly above its resting level of -70 mV. This is because the voltage-gated potassium channels take a little longer to close. This phase is called hyperpolarization. This state does not last long, and, shortly after, the cell's membrane potential returns to its resting level. There is a slight delay before the same neuron can generate another action potential. This short interlude prevents signal interference and is called the refractory period.

While this process sounds long and laborious, the generation of an action potential can be an incredibly rapid event. In some nerves, the velocity of an action potential is as fast as 100 meters per second. However, an action potential can also travel as slowly as under a tenth of a meter per second.

Glia: The Brain's Support System

Types of Glial Cells

The brain is made up of two main types of cells, namely neurons, which were discussed in the previous section, and non-neuronal cells called glial cells. The glial cells can also be referred to as glia or neuroglia. The word glia comes from the Greek word for glue. Glial cells are responsible for nourishing, protecting, and supporting the neurons in the brain and are 10 to 50 times more prevalent than neurons. They are fundamental to the communication between neurons, as well as between neurons and muscle fibers, and regulate important body functions like pH balance and metabolism (Sherrell, 2023). There are four primary types of glial cells in the CNS, specifically astroglia (astrocytes), oligodendroglia (oligodendrocytes), ependymal cells (ependymocytes), and microglia. Within the peripheral nervous system (PNS), which is all the nerves in the body apart from the brain and spinal cord, there are two main types of glial cells: Schwann cells and satellite cells. Glial cells are functionally important in both the central and peripheral nervous systems, which means if they stop operating normally, they can cause the development of certain neurological disorders.

Functions of Glial Cells

Glial cells function mainly to ensure the nervous system is kept healthy and functioning effectively. Because they are directly and indirectly responsible for structurally supporting neurons, transmitting electrical signals, protecting neurons from injury and illness, and regulating the movement of substances between the brain and blood, glial cells are considered the primary functioning cells of the nervous system.

The four main types of glial cells function in the CNS as follows:

1. *Astroglia or astrocytes:* The most abundant type of glial cells, astrocytes are quite literally the support system for the central nervous system. Found throughout the spinal cord, brain, and retina, astrocytes are large and star-shaped. These abundant cells regulate homeostasis in the nervous system by acting as the "link" between neurons and blood vessels, effectively modulating the movement of substances between the brain and blood. They also control and manage the concentration of neurotransmitters and ions, affecting the brain's electrical impulses, and neuronal defense and repair (Cherry, 2023). Astrocytes make up more than 25% of the brain's total volume.
2. *Oligodendroglia or oligodendrocytes:* These cells produce myelin, which is a fatty substance that coats neuronal axons, insulating them and allowing the transmission of electrical impulses. Myelin also regulates the speed and efficiency of

nerve impulses, maximizing velocity and maintaining electrical conduction.

3. *Ependymal cells:* Also called ependymocytes, these cells secrete cerebrospinal fluid (CSF). They form the ependyma, which is an epithelial barrier that lines the spinal cord and the brain's ventricles (cavities within the brain that are filled with fluid and are responsible for CSF homeostasis and circulation). Cerebrospinal fluid (CSF) is a clear substance that cushions the brain and the spinal cord, removes waste and harmful molecules, and provides nutrients to neurons.

4. *Microglia:* These cells act like the brain's immune system, protecting the central nervous system from attack by pathogenic organisms. They have a variety of anti-inflammatory and protective functions, constantly monitoring for anything that may present a danger to the brain. Microglia behave similarly to white blood cells (macrophages) and are considered the macrophages of the nervous system. They remove any dead cells, microbes, and other debris, and react to any nervous system injury or infection. These "soldiers" of the brain make up more than 10% of cells in the nervous system.

The two primary glial cells in the PNS are:

1. *Schwann cells:* Functioning in a way similar to the oligodendrocytes, which can only be found in the CNS, certain Schwann cells also produce myelin. This fatty sheath surrounds the nerves in the PNS and creates an insulating effect, which assists in increasing the speed and effectiveness of electrical transmission and conduction. Schwann cells also contribute to the regeneration of nerve fibers, assisting new axons to grow within the gaps of damaged and digested axons. By promoting the growth of new axons, Schwann cells ensure the continuous transmission of electrical impulses along neurons.

2. *Satellite cells:* Much like their name, satellite cells can be found around neuronal cell bodies in the PNS, where they support and surround these cells and balance chemicals in the cells' environment. Satellite cells also protect neurons from degenerating or dying and supply nutrients to peripheral nerves. They behave similarly to the astrocytes of the CNS by regulating the environment around peripheral neurons and providing them with nutrients and structural support. They also remove toxic and harmful substances from neurons by absorbing them.

The Role of Glia in Brain Health

Glial cells play an integral role in maintaining brain health. In summary, glial cells provide the following functions:

1. *Structural support:* Glial cells create and produce structural components to support neurons. These include myelin sheaths that facilitate electrical impulse transmission, as well as physical structures that support brain tissue. By regulating the concentration of various molecules that surround neurons, glial cells provide them with structural support and integrity.
2. *Exchange of nutrients and waste:* Neurons require fuel and oxygen to function correctly but also release waste as a result. Glial cells work to make sure that neurons receive the nutrients they require and remove the metabolic waste that is produced. This exchange is facilitated between the neurons and the blood.
3. *Regulating neurotransmission:* Neurotransmitters are the molecules that transmit signals between neurons, or between neurons and other body parts like muscles or glands. Also called the nervous system's chemical messengers, neurotransmitters allow communication to occur across synapses. Glial cells regulate the levels of neurotransmitters to maintain balance and ensure synapses

can function effectively. They do this by removing and recycling used neurotransmitters.

4. *Immune response:* Certain glial cells detect and respond to any potential pathogens or injuries. These microglia are responsible for monitoring the nervous system for toxins, dead cells, or bacteria and removing them. Often, microglia respond to injury or disease by causing inflammation, which prompts the healing process.

5. *Homeostasis:* Homeostasis is the regulation of the concentration of hormones, ions, and other chemicals in the nervous system. Glial cells maintain neuronal balance to regulate brain metabolism by storing molecules and releasing them when required.

6. *Synaptic function:* Healthy glial cells support neural and synaptic plasticity, or the ability of the neurons and synapses in the brain to change, adapt, and strengthen. Synapses are the connections between neurons that allow electrical messages or stimuli to pass between them. Glial cells assist with brain development by removing ineffective or unnecessary synapses and allowing the brain to function effectively. Synaptic plasticity has a significant impact on the brain's ability to learn and remember, as well as processing external stimuli and senses, and regulating voluntary and involuntary bodily movements. Various neurological disorders can occur with dysfunctional synaptic plasticity, such as Alzheimer's and Parkinson's disease.

BRAIN DEVELOPMENT

Prenatal Brain Development

There are three main stages of prenatal brain development, divided according to stages of gestation. The first stage is called the germinal stage and takes place within the first two weeks of embryonic development. The second stage is referred to as the embryonic stage and takes place between the third and eighth week after conception. The last stage, which is the fetal stage, starts after the ninth week and continues until birth. As the brain grows and develops various regions of the brain responsible for motor control and other activities, the fetus will start moving, breathing, and swallowing. The brain will continue to develop after birth and into childhood, a process called postnatal brain development.

Embryonic Stage

Once the germinal stage is complete, the cell division that took place to form a blastocyst has resulted in the development of a mass of cells called the embryo. The brain already begins to develop in the embryo with the development of a neural plate. The neural plate is the foundation of the nervous system and after a few weeks will form the neural tube, which will eventually become the brain and spinal cord.

During the embryonic stage of vertebrate brain development, a neural crest is formed, which is a fold on the neural plate. The neural plate is formed when two types of epithelial cells join together, namely neural and epidermal ectoderms. A hollow tube is created on the neural plate as two ridges grow and fold into one another. This process is called neurulation. Various cell types are produced by the neural crest during the embryonic stage. Collectively, these cells are called neural crest cells, which will later differentiate to form tissues and organs like bones, muscles, cartilage, and neurons and glia of the peripheral nervous system and gastrointestinal or enteric system.

Once specific neurons form, which occurs around six weeks after conception, they migrate to specific areas of the brain where they form early neural networks by developing synaptic connections. Also, at this stage in pregnancy, the neural tube has now closed, and the brain consists of three regions. The forebrain will become the cerebrum, which processes thinking and problem-solving. The midbrain will process sensory information like vision and hearing. Finally, the hindbrain will become the cerebellum, which will be responsible for motor control and the medulla oblongata, which will process involuntary activities like heart rate and blood pressure.

Formation of the Brain From the Neural Tube

The neural tube forms as the neural plate folds in on itself. This occurs in the embryo within the first month of conception. The neural tube closes completely by the seventh week, or the fourth week of embryonic development.

The beginning of several brain regions occurs during the fifth week of embryonic development. This occurs with the growth of vesicles or sacs at the cranial end, or cephalad portion, of the neural tube. Initially, three primary vesicles develop, which then become five secondary vesicles. The three primary vesicles that form the three early brain regions are called the prosencephalon (forebrain), the mesencephalon (midbrain), and the rhombencephalon (hindbrain). These vesicles later split to form the following five vesicles in the five-week-old embryo:

- The telencephalon, which becomes the cerebrum and splits from the prosencephalon.
- The diencephalon, which also splits from the prosencephalon, and later forms the thalamus, hypothalamus, and epithalamus.
- The mesencephalon, which becomes the midbrain.
- The metencephalon, which splits from the rhombencephalon to become the pons and cerebellum.
- The myelencephalon, which also splits from the rhombencephalon to become the medulla oblongata.

The other end of the neural tube, the caudal end, develops into the spinal cord.

Fetal Brain Growth

Within the first three months of development, the brain of a fetus will make up almost 50% of its weight. This is the most important period in brain development.

In the second trimester, the brain starts sending electrical impulses to the muscles of the chest and the diaphragm, an imitation of breathing. At this stage, the brain starts developing fissures and folds called sulci and gyri, and the layer of the cerebral cortex starts thickening. The axons of neurons start becoming myelinated, where a fatty substance called myelin forms on axons to promote the transfer of electric stimuli. The process of myelination will continue as a child grows.

As the brain grows and the electrical stimuli increase, the fetus will start moving. The development of a more complex neural network will cause reflexive actions, as neurons now connect. By the end of the sixth month of pregnancy, the fetus' brainstem, which is just above the spinal cord, should be almost fully developed.

The third trimester shows a tripling in the size of the brain, characterized by rapid growth and development of neurons. As the cerebrum grows, the right and left brain become separated. The fetus will start moving more and more as the parts of the brain that control movement, namely the cerebellum, grow and develop rapidly. During this time, the cerebral cortex, which is responsible for higher cognitive abilities and sensory perception and processing, starts to grow and develop. The fetus will now be able to hear, smell, and taste.

Postnatal Brain Development

At birth, a baby's brain has grown and developed more than 100 billion neurons, which means a growth rate of approximately 250,000 neurons per minute during pregnancy. However, the brain does not stop growing or developing after birth. In fact, the size of the brain increases by almost four times by the time a child is around the age of four or five. In the first year of a baby's life, the cerebellum triples in size as motor skills develop rapidly and sight changes from blurry and dim to full binocular vision. When a baby is born, they already have the ability to use basic reflexive movements like sucking and grasping. They are also able to use all five senses.

By the age of three months, growth in the hippocampus allows a baby to recognize objects and faces, while areas of the frontal and temporal lobes consolidate language skills.

In the baby's second year, its language abilities will increase dramatically, a result of the development of the regions of the brain responsible for speaking and communicating. It is also at this age that a baby starts to develop self-awareness, emotions, and other high-order cognitive abilities. As the prefrontal cortex grows and strengthens, these complex cognitive abilities improve.

By the time a child reaches five years of age, their brain has developed to 90% of its final structural and functional abilities. This is because, at these early stages, a child's brain is highly plastic, meaning it can adapt and reorganize quickly and easily. It is crucial to provide a child with a stable, positive, and supportive environment during this critical period to allow for healthy brain development. While genetic influences play a significant role in prenatal brain development, environmental factors contribute strongly to postnatal brain development and future cognitive and behavioral abilities.

Synaptogenesis and Pruning

During the development of the brain, which starts in the womb, neurons form connections with one another to facilitate the transmission of electrical impulses. This allows information to be transferred to and from the central and peripheral nervous systems. Neurons communicate with each other and with glands, tissue, and muscles through special junctions called synapses. The process by which new synaptic contacts are made is called synaptogenesis. Synapotogenesis starts during gestation of the fetus and continues throughout childhood, and into early adolescence.

There is a significant increase in the development of synaptic connections, or synaptogenesis, in early brain development. This burst in the amount of synaptic connections occurs in young children of two to three years of age and corresponds to a critical or sensitive period in brain development. It is at this stage that the brain starts forming neural networks that contribute to higher cognitive and behavioral functions. Once a synaptic connection is formed, it can be strengthened by repetitive use of that pathway. However, if that neural network is not regularly used or exercised, that synaptic connection can be weakened and even lost.

If synapses are not actively used or strengthened, the brain regards them as irrelevant or unnecessary and works to remove them. This process begins shortly after the rapid explosion in synaptogenesis and is called synaptic pruning. Although it starts early in brain development, heightened synaptic pruning occurs between the ages of two and sixteen. During this period, the brain sees a significant decrease in the number of synapses, which is a reduction of almost half the amount of extra synapses. Synaptic pruning slows down during adolescence and into adulthood. It is an essential process required to remove redundant synapses to keep the brain functioning efficiently over time.

Critical Periods

Critical periods, also called sensitive periods, refer to stages in the early development of a child's brain where brain plasticity is at its maximum. It is also when the brain needs to be exposed to a variety of sensory information. This then allows the facilitation of ideal cortical networks to effectively process the environment. The development of a child's brain after birth can be divided into four main stages. One of the most critical periods in a baby's development is from birth to two years of age. It is during this stage that the brain doubles in size. Also called the sensorimotor stage, it is a crucial time for the development of the prefrontal cortex and the cerebellum. It is now that a baby starts to develop motor skills like lifting its head and sitting unaided. It is also at this stage that the baby begins to develop a trusting relationship with its primary caregivers.

During the baby's next few years, from ages two to seven, the brain is still growing at a rapid rate. This is the preoperational stage, where a child develops language and communication skills, as well as short- and long-term memory, logic, and reasoning. From the ages of seven to eleven, a child goes through the concrete operational stage, where they start becoming aware of other's emotions and start developing logical thought processes. Lastly, the formal operational stage, which occurs from ages eleven all through to adulthood is when a child develops abstract cognitive abilities. A person's brain is only fully developed when they reach 25 years of age.

Immediately post-birth, called the ante-natal period, the newborn baby will develop attachment behaviors based on their experience. During an infant's first three years, positive relationships with caregivers can foster a sense of support. However, this is when the brain is most susceptible to toxic environmental and relationship stressors. Over the next two years, a foundation in brain development is built, on which other sequential developmental levels will develop. By the time a child goes to school, they will be primed by their home environment, and this will impact how they cope with a learning environment. Once a child reaches adolescence, the brain will focus on developing those regions that were previously used the most in childhood. This is also referred to as "pruning" or removal of unnecessary or unused synaptic connections in the brain. Again, this influences how a teenager responds to their environment.

Impact of Early Experiences on Brain Development

Early postnatal brain development is extensive and rapid. Strengthening of neural networks, myelination to improve the transfer of information, neural growth and plasticity, and an improvement in complex cognitive processes means that early experiences have a significant impact on later neural, behavioral, and cognitive abilities. While negative experiences at an early age can negatively impact brain development, this is also a period of opportunity to assist positive brain growth and development.

Sengpiel (n.d.) suggests there are various critical periods in a child's postnatal brain development where the environmental experiences it receives will determine its abilities later in life. He also believes that different critical periods in brain development align with the development of brain functions. For example, the development of ocular functions in the brain occurs at birth in humans, who are born with their eyes open.

Extensive research on early brain development in children suggests that early experiences significantly affect brain development. An overwhelmingly positive early experience will result in optimal brain development. Further, optimal brain development allows the full development of various cognitive, behavioral, and emotional skills and abilities. Providing a solid base for sequential brain development will ensure the effective development of high-order and complex skills. Early childhood development experts emphasize that while children will inevitably be exposed to various environmental stressors, a safe, secure and positive relationship with primary caregivers can buffer against these stressors and increase resilience in the child. Unhealthy, negative, and toxic relationships with caregivers in the early stages of a child's life can severely impact the brain's development, preventing and damaging later key functions.

BRAIN REGIONS AND LOBES

The Four Main Brain Lobes

The cerebrum is the largest part of the brain and is divided into two hemispheres, each of which has one of a pair of lobes. There are four main brain lobes, divided from one another by grooves in the surface of the brain called fissures. Each lobe is further divided into smaller sections, each of which has very specific functions.

Frontal Lobe

The frontal lobes are the largest of the four and are found directly behind the forehead. They govern voluntary motor skills and both intellectual and behavioral functions. Also controlled by the frontal lobes are personality, mood, memory, emotions, problem-solving, planning, judgement, self-awareness, and concentration. Social and moral reasoning also come from the frontal lobes.

Found within the frontal lobes is Broca's area, an area of the brain that controls speech and writing. Broca's area, usually located on the left side of the frontal lobe, is essential for fluency and producing language. The frontal lobes are considered a crucial section of the brain responsible for human cognition and behaviour and influence various executive processes like achieving long-term goals and managing day-to-day tasks and planning. They assist in filtering out any distractions while focusing on relevant information.

Working memory, which is the storage and manipulation of information, occurs predominantly in the dorsolateral prefrontal cortex, a specific region in the frontal lobes that also participates in the regulation of emotions and other behavior. Damage to areas of the frontal lobes can result in changes in personality, behavior, temperament, and social interactions, as these lobes, when acting effectively, can inhibit reckless and impulsive behaviors. Parts of the frontal lobes are also involved in the recognition of smell.

Parietal Lobe

The parietal lobes are found in the center of the brain between the occipital and frontal lobes. Both parietal lobes of the brain receive and interpret signals and stimuli simultaneously, through the functional sensory area of the lobe called the primary somatosensory cortex. These include stimuli such as sight, hearing, motor, and sensory, which are received from sensory receptors in the skin, as well as proprioceptors in muscles, tendons, and joints, which govern the awareness of the position of the body. This means that pain and touch in the body are also interpreted by the parietal lobes.

The parietal lobes allow humans to give meaning to objects by interpreting new information received and accessing memory functions. They also allow people to identify objects, as well as understand where an object is in comparison with the body and the surrounding environment, called the spatial relationship. Other functions of the parietal lobes include spatial and visual perception, temperature perception, and word and language interpretation. The parietal lobes allow a person to recognize that their body parts belong to them and to develop and engage the body's position and boundaries. The intraparietal sulcus is an area within the parietal lobes that plays a role in processing numbers and mathematical calculations, as well as numerical estimations. Most importantly, the parietal lobes are responsible for prioritizing received stimuli and information to initiate action and perception, making them crucial in a variety of cognitive and behavioral functions.

Temporal Lobe

Located close to the base of the skull on either side of the brain, and also known as the neocortex, the temporal lobes can be divided into the ventral (bottom) and lateral (side) of each hemisphere. Within the temporal lobes, one finds Wernicke's area, which is responsible for understanding written and spoken language and is critical for speech production. The temporal lobes are involved in a variety of cognitive and behavioral functions by processing auditory and visual stimuli, assisting with spatial navigation and orientation through the entorhinal cortex, forming meaningful sentences, and consolidating and forming long-term memories. Short-term memories are also encoded within the temporal lobes, and stored memories are retrieved through this part of the brain.

While the main area of visual processing is found in the occipital lobes, the temporal lobes play a role in complex, higher-order visual processes such as recognizing and interpreting faces, scenes, and objects. This means that the temporal lobes are also crucial in social cognition, which includes empathizing with others and attributing suitable emotional and mental states to oneself and others. The amygdala, which is found within the medial temporal lobe, is important for emotional regulation and fear as well as pleasurable emotional learning. Other functions of the temporal lobes include musical rhythm, smell recognition, short-term memory, and language. The lobes on the right side of the brain function mainly in recognizing objects and faces, and overall visual memory, while the left side is involved predominantly in verbal memory and assists in remembering and understanding language. The rear portion of the temporal lobe is responsible for processing other people's reactions and emotions.

Occipital Lobe

The main role of the occipital lobes, which are found at the back of the brain, is to perceive, process, and interpret visual stimuli. This includes light, motion, shapes, and color. The smallest section of the brain, the occipital lobes receive visual information from the retina of the eye through the optic nerves to process the visual environment. The left side of the lobes is responsible for processing visual stimuli received from the right side of the visual space, while the right side of the lobes processes stimuli from the left side of the visual space. Other visual processes governed by the occipital lobes include depth perception, which interprets the distance between objects in space; visual memory, which is the storage, retrieval, and processing of visual information; and visual imagery, where various objects and scenes can be visualized, even without sensory input.

The occipital lobes are responsible for interpreting and understanding the visual environment around us.

Functions of Each Lobe

As previously mentioned, although each set of lobes in the brain is responsible for certain functions, all parts of the brain work together to understand, interpret, and process various external information and stimuli. Here, we examine how the lobes of the brain work together to perform their complex and interconnected roles in influencing human behavior and cognition.

Motor Control

Motor control is defined as the complex interaction between various systems in the body, including the brain and the spinal cord, that regulates and coordinates voluntary muscle and limb movement. The frontal lobes control voluntary movement. This is mainly done by the primary motor cortex (M1), a region of the cerebral cortex located within the frontal lobe. The anatomical location of the M1 is called the precentral gyrus. The M1 receives signals from various areas in the brain like the cerebellum, via the thalamus, and other cortical regions like the somatosensory area. The larger motor cortex of the frontal lobe also includes the premotor cortex, which is located adjacent to the primary motor cortex, and the supplementary motor area.

The primary motor cortex sends stimuli to either the spinal cord to prompt voluntary movement in the body, or to the brain, to initiate movement of the head and neck. Because it is highly sensitive to stimuli, the primary motor cortex doesn't require a large amount of stimulation for it to initiate movement. The primary motor cortex is arranged in a somatotypical pattern, which means that different regions of this center control specific regions of the body. This is often visually demonstrated by the "motor homunculus," a proportional "topographical" map of body parts and their corresponding regions in the frontal lobe.

The primary motor cortex is composed of pyramidal neurons, which are large upper motor neurons that are triangular. These upper motor neurons emerge from the cerebral cortex of the brain and the brainstem and end in the spinal cord. They connect with lower motor neurons, which leave from the brain and spinal cord and terminate at the muscles to initiate movement.

While the primary motor cortex is responsible for controlling and initiating voluntary, refined, and skilled muscle movements, the premotor cortex controls the preparation of movement. The supplementary motor cortex controls less refined and less focused movements like posture and coordination.

Sensory Processing

In the context of this book, sensory processing refers to the receipt and interpretation of different senses, like visual (sight), auditory (sound), olfactory (smell), gustatory (taste), and tactile (touch). Several lobes are responsible for regulating and controlling overall sensory processing.

1. *Visual processing:* The occipital lobes interpret and process visual information received from the eyes. It uses these signals to work closely with other parts of the brain to interpret what the eyes see. The center of visual processing in the occipital lobe is called the primary visual cortex. Information like motion, colors, and shapes is interpreted here. The occipital lobe not only processes color and shape but also interprets distance and depth perception, as well as spatial processing. It is also involved in recognizing familiar objects and faces and assists in storing memories.

2. *Auditory processing:* The temporal lobe processes sound stimuli. Sound is moved by the auditory nerve in the cochlear of the ear to the primary auditory cortices in the temporal lobes. Like other regions in the brain, the right-hand auditory cortex processes information received by the left ear, and vice versa. The temporal lobe assists in filtering

out unnecessary frequencies and processes pitch and sounds. The right temporal lobe works to process emotional tone in voices, non-verbal sounds, and other auditory information. The left temporal lobe is generally the more dominant lobe and works to store verbal information, process music, and understand language. Wernicke's area is a section of the left temporal lobe that processes spoken language.

3. *Olfactory processing:* The temporal lobe plays a small role in processing certain aspects of smell through the complex olfactory cortex, part of which is located within the temporal lobe. The parietal lobe, which is responsible for processing somatosensory information, also contributes to interpreting the sense of smell.

4. *Gustatory processing:* The temporal lobe is involved in processing stimuli like taste. Because it processes all senses, including smell and touch, the parietal lobe also plays a small role in interpreting the sense of taste.

5. *Tactile processing:* The sense of touch is processed by the parietal lobe. This includes texture, temperature, pressure, and awareness of the position of the body. Also called somatosensory information, the parietal lobe interprets signals received from the body's sensory receptors and processes them.

Language and Communication

Communication is made up of three main components, namely language, speaking, and writing. Because there are various activities involved in speaking and writing, there are several regions of the brain that work together to perceive, process, and interpret communication. For example, to speak coherently in a way that others understand, the brain has to access stored language, link those words together to form sentences that make sense and produce those sounds. Areas of the brain that are largely responsible for speaking and writing include the cerebellum, basal ganglia, the insular cortex with the lateral sulcus, and areas within the parietal and temporal lobe. Interestingly, research suggests that the majority of language processing takes place in the left side of the brain, although the reason for this is still uncertain.

The production, interpretation, and processing of language and speech is done mainly by the temporal and frontal lobes. Broca's area, which is found in the left frontal lobe, plays a role in the formation of sentences to assist with fluency in language and the organizing of speech. It is important for expressing language. Lying close to Broca's area and making up a large section of the temporal lobe, Wernicke's area is responsible for arranging words together based on their meaning to produce comprehensive sentences. Working closely with the basal ganglia, insular cortex, and angular gyrus, Wernicke's area processes the sequence of words and their meaning and context.

Studies on the brain and its role in processing language, speech, and communication have shown that the parietal lobe also plays a minor role in speaking and writing. However, rather than processing and interpreting spoken language, a section of the parietal lobe called the angular gyrus is more responsible for the motor control required for writing (Brownsett and Wise, 2010).

MAPPING THE BRAIN

Historical Methods of Brain Mapping

Before the high-tech methods of brain imaging and mapping, the anatomical structure and related functions of the brain were determined by the effects of trauma on specific regions of the brain (Savoy, 2001). Nowadays, brain mapping is a specialized and technical method of understanding the detailed location of various functions of the brain. It also allows neuroscientists to examine how the brain reacts to external environmental stimuli, and how the brain changes with age and over time. Modern brain mapping also assists scientists and doctors in understanding how mental illness and other brain diseases physically change the brain. Whereas historical brain "mapping" relied on the use of damaged or dead brains, current technology employs sophisticated and non-invasive methods to map the brain.

Phrenology

Modern technology has made it easy to get an understanding of the structure and function of the central nervous system. However, before advanced systems like MRI and CT scans became available today, anatomists, physicians, and other scientists had to rely on simpler methods to try and understand how the brain works. One of the earlier techniques developed in an attempt to diagnose a patient's personality, mental abilities, and behavioral traits was called phrenology.

Now regarded as a pseudoscience, phrenology was founded by German neuroanatomist, Franz Joseph Gall, in the late 1700s. Gall believed that by mapping the contours and shape and size of the skull, one could determine mental and cognitive functions. He asserted that the topography of the skull has a major influence on the shape and structure of the brain, thereby influencing various traits and personality characteristics. Gall attributed several regions of the skull's 'landscape' to various human faculties. For example,

Gall believed that a cheerful person would show two large bumps on the forehead, while lumps above the ears could indicate innate greed. Phrenologists used a crude method of feeling the skull to diagnose various human conditions, like deceitfulness, intelligence, depression, pride, and love. This practice inferred that people were born with various predispositions and morals, relying on potentially offensive generalizations to diagnose disorders amongst different social groups. Interestingly, decades later, Gall was proven correct in his identification of areas of the brain that process word memory and language. While modern neuroscience no longer recognizes the theory of phrenology, it did introduce the concept of brain localization.

Phrenology was later discounted towards the mid-1800s, mostly as a result of its tendency to generalize according to social status, as well as the lack of scientific accuracy and rigor. French physician, Marie Jean Pierre Flourens, was instrumental in disproving Gall's assertion that brain shape was influenced by contours on the skull. These days, phrenology is regarded as a discredited and unscientific theory steeped in racial inequalities.

Early Brain Mapping Techniques

The first understanding of localized brain structure and function was developed by examining diseased and damaged brains. For example, and one of the most famous stories of localized brain damage, is that of Phineas Gage in 1848. An American construction worker, Gage suffered significant head trauma during an industrial accident where an iron rod was driven right through his left cheek, into his brain, and out his skull. Most significantly, he experienced drastic changes to his personality, attributed decades later to damage to his frontal lobe.

Towards the middle of the 20th Century, American-Canadian neurosurgeon, Wilder Graves Penfield, pioneered a relatively non-invasive technique of mapping areas of the brain in live patients. Penfield used the "Montreal Procedure," whereby various regions of the brain were activated while patients were awake, allowing them to react to this stimulation. This procedure allowed Penfield and his colleagues to accurately map the location of speech in the cerebral cortex and memory in the temporal lobes.

Another significant figure in the field of neuroscience and brain mapping is Korbinian Brodmann. Born in Germany in 1868, Brodmann used advanced (for the day) technology to create histological slides of stained human brain tissue. He observed these slides using a microscope to create a map of the cerebral cortex and other parts of the brain by delineating different brain cell types. Brodmann's images were so accurate that they are still widely used in modern neuroscience.

Modern Brain Mapping Techniques

Techniques for mapping brain imagery have progressed significantly from the days of live brain activation and histological slides. These days, brain mapping uses complex technology to generate detailed images of the brain, which are converted into data that can be thoroughly analyzed.

Neuroimaging

Neuroimaging refers to a process of medical imagery whereby images of the central nervous system can be obtained in non-invasive ways. It is also called brain scanning. There are two main branches of neuroimagery, namely functional neuroimagery and structural neuroimagery. As per their names, structural neuroimagery uses various methods to obtain images of the structure, size, and shape of the brain and its different regions. Functional neuroimagery produces data on the brain's function and activity.

There are several methods of obtaining imagery of the central nervous systems, namely computer axial tomography (CAT) or computer tomography (CT) scans, magnetic resonance imaging (MRI), and diffusion tensor-MRI (DTI). One of the more popular methods of structural brain imagery is MRIs. Magnetic Resonance Imaging (MRI) was developed in the early 1970s as a non-invasive method using magnetics and radiofrequency to create detailed, cross-sectional images of the body's soft tissues.

The MRI scanner uses a large magnet to attract the protons in the water molecules of living bodies. It then sends a pulse of radio waves through the body that causes the alignment of these protons to be disrupted. The radio frequency is then turned off, allowing the protons to return to their original positions. As they do this, they emit energy, which is picked up by the scanner to create these images. Magnetic Resonance (MR) scanners can be used to produce images of the structure of the brain, as well as brain activity. Because it does not require radiation to function, MR scans are relatively safe.

Diffusion tensor imaging (DTI) is a form of MRI that uses the movement of water along neurons in the brain as they are activated by magnetic pulses. The images created show the direction of pathways in the brain's neural circuit. It is used to diagnose neurological disorders such as brain tumors, stroke, lesions, and multiple sclerosis.

Computer tomography (CT) imagery is produced by passing X-ray beams through the soft tissues of the body, like the brain. The X-ray waves move around the selected area to provide images from various angles. This creates a cross-sectional image of the organ or tissue under examination. CT scans are used to diagnose structural abnormalities in the brain like stroke, infection, inflammation, lesions, injury, and intracranial hemorrhage.

Functional Neuroimaging

Brain activity is determined by functional neuroimagery systems, of which there are five main techniques, electroencephalography (EEG), positron emission tomography (PET), functional MRI (fMRI), pharmacological MRI (phMRI), and transcranial magnetic stimulation (TMS).

Electroencephalography (EEG) uses electrodes placed on the outside of the skull to pick up electrical signals triggered by brain activity.

Various disorders and illnesses such as brain tumors, stroke, epilepsy, sleep disorders, and encephalitis can be picked up by EEG scans.

In positron emission tomography (PET), markers called radio-tracers are injected into the bloodstream of the patient. The PET scanner picks up changes in the amount of positrons in the tissue as the radiotracers interact with the electrons within the body tissue. This creates an image of the required tissues and organs while active by measuring metabolic activity. PET scans can record changes in brain chemistry and function, and are used to diagnose Alzheimer's disease, epilepsy, brain tumors, and dementia.

Functional MRI (fMRI) scans are used to pick up corresponding activation in areas of the brain while a patient performs various movements and activities. These scans use fluctuations in blood flow, metabolic activity, and oxygenation in the brain in relation to neural activity. As a patient works on a specific task, activity in the brain increases, which causes oxygen and glucose to be used up. Because of this metabolic activity, the brain requires an increase in oxygen, which triggers an increase in blood flow. Those regions of the brain that are activated by the task will require more oxygenated blood than other less active areas. It is this contrast in the blood that is used to produce data and imagery by the fMR scanner. This non-invasive form of brain mapping can detect brain activity as a result of various motor, emotional, cognitive, and sensory activities. A prominent mapping technique in modern neuroscience, fMRI is used to detect various neural disorders and diseases, such as traumatic brain injuries, brain tumors, stroke, and epilepsy. Pharmacological functional MRI (phMRI) scanners use a form of fMRI to produce imagery of activities that occur in the brain with the administration of pharmaceuticals.

Lastly, transcranial magnetic stimulation (TMS) is a process similar to the EEG, whereby electromagnetic coils are applied to the scalp of the patient. Magnetic pulses move through the skull and into the brain to induce electrical currents. Based on the type of magnetic pulse that is applied to the brain tissue, neural activity can either be excited or inhibited. This non-invasive form of neuroimagery is used to treat disorders such as depression, pain, and migraines.

Advances in Brain Connectivity Mapping

Brain connectivity mapping, also called connectomics, is a relatively new field of neuroscience that works to produce a map of neuronal connections in the brain. Connectomics is the study of what is referred to as a 'connectome' or connection matrix, which can be of a single type of neuron or an entire region in the brain. On average, the cerebral cortex or gray matter of the human brain contains about 86 billion neurons. Neurons don't exist in isolation from one another; rather, they are connected by synapses. Research shows that there are approximately 100 trillion synaptic connections between neurons in the brain. Connectomics aims to understand and map various scales of neural connections, from the entire brain network to connections between individual neurons. A comprehensive structural map of the brain's neural circuit can clarify complex brain functions.

Various technologies are being used to study connectomics or brain connectivity. These include fMRI scans, MR spectroscopy (a non-invasive technique using radiofrequency and magnetic fields to produce data on metabolite concentrations), diffusion MRI (dMRI) (similar to DTI), and high-speed serial transmission electron microscopy (EM). Serial transmission EM is a technique whereby high-resolution 3D images are produced by analyzing ultra-thin samples of biological matter that have been embedded in resin. Another method of non-invasive image production is called tractography. Tractography is an advancement in the DTI technique using advanced constrained spherical deconvolution (CSD). Like DTI, tractography uses the diffusion of water molecules in live brain tissue to map white matter fibers, and thereby produce intricate 3D models or maps of the brain's connectomes.

Recent advances in technology and data capture and analyses, using machine learning, have propelled the science of connectomics towards the future. Researchers like Wei-Chung Allen Lee, who is an associate professor of neurology at Harvard Medical School, believe that connectomics will one day assist in understanding how differences in individual connectomes are associated with different behaviors in those individuals. Lee also believes the field of connectomics will help scientists understand fundamental cognitive and behavioral differences across species. He suggests that "common humanity may lie in the shared structure of how our brains are wired" (Caruso, 2023).

In an effort to further the research behind modern brain connectivity mapping, leading scientists created the Human Connectome Project (HCP) in 2009. The aim of HCP is to produce advanced brain connectivity analyses and imaging in an attempt to connect the structure of the human brain with its behavior and function. There are now several research projects that fall under the umbrella of HCP to study the effect of disease, age, and growth on connections in the human brain.

THE CENTRAL NERVOUS SYSTEM

The Brain and Spinal Cord

The central nervous system (CNS) is made up of the brain and spinal cord. So named because it effectively coordinates all bodily activities, the CNS controls both complex functional and cognitive processes like heart rate, blood pressure, emotions, behavior, breathing, and many more. It is sometimes referred to as the body's primary command or control center for its overarching role in processing sensory information and coordinating motor control. The CNS is separate from the peripheral nervous system (PNS), which contains all the nerve fibers that fall outside of the CNS. The PNS passes information from the body's tissues, muscles, and organs to the CNS for processing.

Anatomy of the Spinal Cord

The spinal cord is the connection point between the brain and the rest of the body. It emerges from the cranial end of the brain as an extension of the medulla oblongata of the brainstem. Running along almost the entire length of the spine, the spinal cord is a tube-like structure made up of white and gray matter, protected by the meninges and cerebrospinal fluid. As with the brain, the spinal cord meninges is made up of three layers, the dura mater, arachnoid mater, and pia mater. The delicate spinal cord is contained within the spine (vertebral column). It terminates at the L2 vertebra, which is part of the lumbar spine and is the last vertebra to contain spinal cord tissue. There are thirty-one spinal nerves that arise from the spinal cord and travel to the rest of the body.

Functions of the Spinal Cord

The spinal cord has five major functions. It transmits electrical stimuli between the brain and the body, allowing the two to communicate with one another. In this way, it is the primary communication center between the brain and the peripheral nervous system. It also plays a part in coordinating voluntary motor control by relaying motor commands from the brain to the body's muscles, glands, and other tissues. The spinal cord collects sensory information from the PNS and relays it to the brain so that various inputs like pain, spatial awareness, temperature, and touch can be processed. Any automatic functions of the body, like digestion, breathing, heart rate, and blood pressure are regulated by the spinal cord so that homeostasis in the body can be maintained. Lastly, the spinal cord coordinates information between neurons responsible for generating involuntary and rapid reflexive actions like blinking of the eyes, coughing, and muscle contractions. These important automatic reflexes protect the body from external harm, such as pulling your hand away from a hot stovetop.

Brain-Spinal Cord Communication

The brain and the spinal cord are connected to one another by a network of neurons that move through the brainstem. The brainstem, which is made up of the pons and medulla oblongata gives rise to the spinal cord through the medulla. Essentially, the brainstem acts as the "relay center," transmitting information between the rest of the brain and the spinal cord. Neural fibers run from the brain and bundle together to form the spinal cord. The spinal cord takes information received by peripheral nerves that spread throughout the body and sends it to and from the brain.

Spinal nerves are made up of dorsal and ventral roots. The dorsal roots of these nerves emerge from the posterior part of the spinal cord, while the ventral roots spring from the anterior area of the spinal cord. Dorsal roots primarily contain sensory neural axons, also called afferent axons. Afferent axons receive information from sensory receptors in the body and transmit them to the spinal cord. From the spinal cord, these signals are moved to the brain for processing. Ventral roots of spinal neurons consist of motor neuron axons (also called efferent axons) and pass information from the spinal cord to muscles, glands, and organs of the body. Simply put, efferent axons send signals from the brain through the spinal cord and to the rest of the body, while afferent axons receive signals from the body and send them back to the brain through the spinal cord for processing.

Protection and Support

Meninges

The meninges are made up of three protective layers of membrane that cover the brain and spinal cord, the dura mater, the arachnoid mater, and the pia mater. Often referred to as the meningeal membranes, these three layers protect the brain and spinal cord, also providing support for a network of nerves, blood vessels, and cerebrospinal fluid. The meninges act as a shock absorber and is mainly responsible for anchoring and protecting the brain from physical trauma and infections. It also contains a network of major blood vessels like the middle meningeal artery that brings blood to the central nervous system. The meninges prevent the brain from excessive movement in the skull and provides support and stability to both the brain and spinal cord. There are various conditions that can affect the meninges, including infections like meningitis, bleeding within the different layers of the meninges, and tumors and growths.

1. *Dura mater:* The name dura mater is derived from the Latin for "tough mother." This thick, strong, tough, and leathery membranous layer is found between the brain and spinal cord and the arachnoid mater. It is the outer layer of the meninges that is made up of a double layer of connective tissue. The first layer of connective tissue connects the dura mater to the skull, while the lower layer connects to the arachnoid mater. The dural venous sinuses are a system of drainage channels that allow the circulation of blood and cerebrospinal fluid to and from your brain. There is a space between the skull of the brain and the dura mater called the epidural space.
2. *Arachnoid mater:* Found between the dura mater and the pia mater, the arachnoid mater is the middle layer of the

meninges. It is thin and fibrous. The word arachnoid, which means spider, comes from the appearance of this layer, which has a network of connective tissue that attaches to the pia mater like spidery threads that bridge the space between the arachnoid mater and the pia mater. There is a layer of cerebrospinal fluid between the arachnoid mater and the dura mater that is called the subdural space. There are no blood vessels or nerves in the arachnoid mater. The arachnoid mater and pia mater are collectively known as the leptomeninges.

3. *Pia mater:* The third layer of the meninges and the one closest to the brain and spinal cord is called the pia mater. The name pia mater comes from the Latin for "tender mother," due to its delicate and thin consistency. It is tightly wrapped around the contours of the brain and the spinal cord and supplies the brain with blood through a network of blood vessels. The space between the arachnoid mater and pia mater is called the subarachnoid space, which is filled with cerebrospinal fluid and acts as a cushion for the brain. The pia mater also allows the spinal cord to remain firm.

Cerebrospinal Fluid

The cerebrospinal fluid (CSF), which is clear and colourless, is made up of a substance similar to plasma and provides support and cushioning to the brain and spinal cord. It is produced by the ventricles in the brain, which are hollow, fluid-filled cavities. Within the ventricles, CSF is made by the choroid plexuses, small knot-like capillaries that hang from the roof of the ventricles. CSF is circulated within the brain by passing through the interventricular foramina, from the lateral ventricles into the third ventricle. It then moves from the third ventricle and into the fourth ventricle through the cerebral or central aqueduct. The greatest quantity of CSF flows within the subarachnoid space, the area between the arachnoid mater and pia mater. Structures called the arachnoid villi, which are found in the superior sagittal sinus, are responsible for recycling CSF. Generally, the volume of CSF and subsequent pressure within the central nervous system remains balanced, with continuous production and absorption. CSF performs five major roles in the brain and spinal cord:

1. *Shock absorption:* The CSF provides cushioning and support against mechanical injury to the brain by absorbing any impacts or shock.
2. *Buoyancy:* The brain is supported within the skull by CSF, which also prevents it from pushing up against the hard outer skull structure.
3. *Transport of nutrients:* CSF delivers nutrients like glucose and oxygen to the brain and spinal cord. It also flushes out metabolic waste.
4. *Homeostasis:* The balance of various substances in the brain and spinal cord like proteins and ions is regulated by the CSF to ensure optimal functioning of the central nervous system.
5. *Protection from infection:* The CSF is partly responsible for preventing harmful substances and pathogens from entering the tissue of the central nervous system.

Any blockages or disruptions to the movement or production of CSF can cause it to build up and collect in the brain ventricles. This can cause neurological disorders like meningitis (infection of the meninges) or hydrocephalus (enlargement of the ventricles). A build-up of CSF in the spinal cord can cause a disorder called syringomyelia.

Blood-Brain Barrier

The meninges and CSF provide physical protection to the brain and the spinal cord. The blood-brain barrier (BBB) provides protection of the CNS against pathogens and toxins in the blood, preventing infections. The BBB is a collective term for several structures that form this protective barrier. It is responsible for the movement of substances between the brain and blood vessels. While this barrier excludes harmful substances from reaching the brain from the blood, it also allows crucial substances like nutrients to enter the brain.

The BBB was discovered in the late 19th Century by scientists Paul Elrich and Edwin Goldman. They noted that colored dye injected into the blood of a mouse did not stain the tissues of the brain or spinal cord, although it colored other bodily tissues. While researchers at that stage were uncertain of how the barrier functioned, it was only in the 1960s that researchers discovered the physical layer that makes up the BBB.

The BBB consists of a semi-permeable protective membrane filled with various structures like receptors, transporters, and pumps that protect the nervous system from pathogens and other harmful or toxic substances. Because it controls the entry and exit of substances between the blood vessels and the brain or spinal cord, it also assists in maintaining homeostasis in the CNS. The BBB helps the brain to maintain effective metabolic activity and neuronal function and ensures integrity of its microenvironment. In essence, the BBB separates the brain from the rest of the body, regulating anything that it could be exposed to through the blood. The functions of the BBB in the CNS can be summarised as follows:

1. *Homeostasis:* Much like the CSF, the BBB regulates the concentration of various molecules and substances like ions, hormones, nutrients, water, and neurotransmitters in the brain.
2. *Nutrient transportation:* The BBB allows essential nutrients like glucose and amino acids, as well as oxygen, to move from the blood to the brain in a controlled manner.
3. *Protection:* Harmful substances like pathogens, toxins, and large molecules are prevented by the BBB from entering the brain from the bloodstream, preventing damage and infections.
4. *Immunity:* The BBB prevents excessive immune responses in the brain to prevent inflammation.

The structure that allows the BBB to restrict and allow the movement of substances and molecules between the brain and the bloodstream is called the endothelial tight junction. Within the blood vessels of the brain, specialized capillary endothelial cells are placed very closely together to form "tight junctions," which act to restrict the movement of certain substances. Other structures like astrocytes and pericytes within the BBB assist in facilitating communication within the cells that form the barrier to change its permeability and maintain regulation. Overall, the BBB is essential in balancing the brain's environment for effective functioning, permitting the movement of essential nutrients and other substances, and preventing pathogens and toxins from entering the brain.

SUBCORTICAL STRUCTURES

The Limbic System

The limbic system is a part of the central nervous system (CNS). It is a highly researched area of the brain and is often described as the "primitive brain," as it regulates behaviors critical for survival, such as feeding and the flight-or-fight response. The limbic system forms a network of structures consisting of the hippocampus, amygdala, cingulate gyrus, hypothalamus, and basal ganglia. It is involved in regulating various behavioral, emotional, and physical functions in the body. It is found within the temporal lobe and lies beneath the cerebral cortex. The limbic system is responsible for processing short- and long-term memories, learning, regulating emotions, involuntary motor functions, and maintaining homeostasis.

Hippocampus

The hippocampus and amygdala are the two main structures of the limbic system. The hippocampus is embedded within the temporal lobe of the brain and is a complex structure of densely packed nerve fibers. Also known as the memory center of the brain, the hippocampus is responsible for consolidating and forming new memories and storing these memories within the cerebral cortex. The hippocampus coordinates two different types of memories: declarative memories and spatial memories. Declarative memories refer to those that require learning and memorizing facts. Memories of spatial relationships help people to navigate their environment based on memories of previous experiences.

Amygdala

The amygdala is another of the two main structures of the limbic system. It is found adjacent to the hippocampus, and, like many brain regions, comes as a pair. The amygdala is responsible for regulating emotions related to memory. Sometimes simplistically referred to as the "fear center," the amygdala has a key function in processing and cementing memories based on fear, usually based on just a few repetitions of the fearful event or reaction. This almond-shaped structure assists the brain in avoiding fearful stimuli by employing the "fight-or-flight" response. It also processes other emotions such as anxiety, anger, and happiness.

Thalamus

The thalamus sorts out any sensory information received by the body and sends it to the correct area of the cerebral cortex for processing. It is located on top of the brainstem. As with the hypothalamus, the thalamus regulates emotional reactivity and is closely linked with other structures within the limbic system. The thalamus has a major role in relaying all sensory stimuli, besides the olfactory senses, that are received from the body to the brain for processing in the cerebral cortex. As a result of acting as the "relay center" of the brain, the thalamus allows the brain to prioritize important information and filter out the rest. Because it is deeply connected to other parts of the limbic system, the thalamus plays a role in various cognitive processes, as well as memory and consciousness.

Hypothalamus

The main function of the hypothalamus is to maintain homeostasis in the body. Homeostasis refers to a steady internal state, where functions like heart rate, hunger, thirst, blood pressure, and body temperature are regulated and balanced. The hypothalamus receives information from various parts of the brain, as well as from sensory stimuli, to maintain this steady internal state and adjust bodily functions as required. This small structure is found in the middle of the brain. It also works closely with the pituitary gland to control the production of hormones in female ovaries, male testes, pancreas, adrenal glands, and thyroid. The hypothalamus plays a critical role in regulating various bodily functions like the sleep-wake cycle, emotions, sex drive, growth, thirst, and weight control.

Basal Ganglia

The term basal ganglia collectively refers to a cluster of brain structures responsible for several bodily processes like motor control, learning, and emotions. Rather than referring to a specific anatomical structure, the grouping of these cells is related more to their function. This group of nuclei coordinates different areas of the brain to process higher-order cognitive functions, such as reinforcement, problem-solving, and regulation. The basal ganglia is formed from six structures, namely the ventral pallidum, subthalamic nucleus, putamen, substantia nigra, globus pallidus, and caudate nucleus. While called the basal ganglia, this structure is composed of both ganglia and nuclei.

Role in Motor Control

Traditionally, the basal ganglia were thought to be primarily responsible for controlling movements like balance and eye movement. New research now shows that this group of structures also regulates executive functions, as well as emotions and behavior. This group of cells is an integral component of the neural chain that controls and regulates any voluntary movements. The basal ganglia receives information from the brain and filters out unnecessary signals so that only certain muscle movements are initiated when required. Therefore, the basal ganglia mainly play an inhibitory role in voluntary movement by reducing exaggerated movements.

The basal ganglia is part of a feedback circuit, which regulates the activation of various parts of the brain that control movement and motor control. Once the need for movement is sparked in the brain, the basal ganglia analyzes the requirements and then inhibits or facilitates necessary motor control pathways. Working with other limbic system regions such as the thalamus as well as the brainstem, the basal ganglia then regulates the magnitude, timing, and direction of movement. This ensures that all movements are goal-directed and adaptive.

While the cerebral cortex is the "control center" of voluntary motor control, the basal ganglia ensure that movements are refined and modulated so that movement that occurs within the muscles is precise. The six components of the basal ganglia are each responsible for specific functions in voluntary motor control:

1. *The striatum:* This unit receives excitatory inputs from the cerebral cortex and relays them to other sections of the basal ganglia nuclei to modulate motor output.
2. *The caudate nucleus:* This C-shaped nucleus collates spatial information that is received from sensory receptors in the body to tell the thalamus what it needs to do to refine movement in response to the various stimuli. In this way, it assists in regulating body posture, movement, accuracy, and speed.
3. *The putamen:* The putamen utilizes dopamine to fine-tune and regulate various voluntary motor functions.
4. *The globus pallidus:* This subcortical structure balances voluntary movements to ensure that they are smooth and precise. The globus pallidus regulates both excitatory and inhibitory actions of the cerebellum to fine-tune motor control.
5. *The subthalamic nucleus:* Also known as Luys' body, this nucleus is thought to regulate the entire basal ganglia to modulate planned motor movements. However, its exact function is currently unknown.
6. *The substantia nigra:* This motor nucleus consists of two parts. One of them, the pars compacta, which provides output to the basal ganglia network, is responsible for supplying dopamine to the system. A depletion of dopamine from the pars compacta results in movement disorders such as Parkinson's disease.

Implications in Parkinson's Disease

Damage to the basal ganglia can result in disorders such as tremors and other involuntary movements. This includes movement conditions like Parkinson's disease. Parkinson's disease falls under the umbrella of parkinsonism, which is a collective term for neurological disorders that are defined by too much or too little movement, or a combination of both. Parkinson's is the most common of the parkinsonism disorders affected by dysfunction of the basal ganglia. Research suggests that Parkinson's disease can affect up to one percent of the world's population over the age of sixty.

Parkinson's disease is one of several movement disorders that is primarily caused by a dysfunction of the production of dopamine and disruption of the effective functioning of the basal ganglia. Because the symptoms of Parkinson's disease only present later in life, it is referred to as a neurodegenerative disorder. One of the most common neurodegenerative disorders in the world, it is associated with slowness in voluntary movement, rigidity, tremors at rest, mood disorders, sleep dysfunction, and a loss of smell.

Parkinson's disease is mainly identified by issues like resting tremors and rigidity, which is an increase in muscle tone. It is also characterized by two forms of movements, specifically bradykinesia, which is the decrease in speed of voluntary movements, and hypokinesia, the lack of spontaneous movements.

Reduced production of dopamine from the input nuclei of the basal ganglia creates an excess of activity in the subthalamic nucleus (STN). This then creates tremors and slow movements. Dopamine, which is an important neurotransmitter, assists in fine-tuning motor control. The reduction in dopamine secretion is caused by the loss of dopaminergic neurons in the substantia nigra of the basal ganglia. Over time, further degeneration of certain sections of the basal ganglia can result in psychiatric disorders such as depression and dementia.

There are several potential causes for the onset of Parkinson's disease. These include exposure to pesticides and herbicides, genetics, and damage to the nuclei of the thalamus.

The Brainstem

There are three main descending components to the brainstem, namely the midbrain, the pons, and the medulla oblongata. The cerebellum and spinal cord are linked to the cerebrum through the brainstem. Located at the base of the brain, the brainstem coordinates basic physiological processes critical for survival, such as consciousness, sleep, breathing, heart rate, and blood pressure. It consists of both gray and white matter. All except two of the twelve cranial nerves emerge from the nerve nuclei in the gray matter of the brainstem. The white matter is made up of afferent and efferent axons that arise from cell bodies and carry information to and from the brain.

Medulla Oblongata, Pons, and Midbrain

The midbrain is the most superior of the three brainstem structures, connecting the pons with the forebrain (the cerebrum). Next in anatomically descending order is the pons. The pons is found between the midbrain and the medulla. The medulla links the pons and the spinal cord.

1. *Midbrain:* The smallest of the three brainstem structures, the midbrain also contains nuclei of the substantia nigra at its base, linking it to the basal ganglia network. The midbrain (also known as the mesencephalon), is comprised of a posterior "roof" called the tectum. The word tectum comes from the Latin word for roof. The tectum contains several structures called colliculi that are responsible for visual and auditory processing. At the point where the midbrain meets the pons is a pair of cerebral peduncles. It is from the cerebral peduncles that the oculomotor neuron runs.
2. *Pons:* The pons is the largest section of the brainstem. The word pons is derived from the Latin word for "bridge," referring to its pathway from the cerebrum, through the medulla, and into the spinal cord. Cranial nerves are

responsible for motor commands such as chewing and facial expressions, and sensory nerves that transmit sensory information like pain, temperature, and touch, originate in the pons. The pons also gives rise to the nuclei for several cranial nerves, which regulate functions like swallowing, hearing, sensations in the face, and balance. These are the trigeminal, abducens, facial, and vestibulocochlear nerves (CN V to VIII).

3. *Medulla oblongata:* The most inferior of the three brainstem structures, the medulla oblongata exits the foramen magnum, an opening in the skull, to emerge into the spinal cord. The medulla contains the nucleus of the solitary tract, which is a nucleus responsible for regulating vital bodily functions necessary for survival such as heart rate, blood pressure, and digestion. It also controls several involuntary activities such as coughing, sneezing, and vomiting.

Vital Functions and Reflexes

The brainstem is responsible for regulating and modulating various bodily processes that are vital to survival. Several major nerve pathways occur in the brainstem that regulate movement, autonomic functions, and sleep. A nerve pathway is a sequence of nerves that transmit information throughout the body. There are three main nerve pathways found in the brainstem. The spinothalamic tract transmits sensory messages from the spinal cord to the thalamus. The corticospinal tract relays information from the cerebral cortex to the spinal cord, from where it moves to the muscles. The spinocerebellar tract regulates balance and posture by sending messages from the cerebellum to the spinal cord.

While the brainstem uses various neural tracts to send messages back and forth between the body, spinal cord, and brain, it also employs neurotransmitters to control complex functions. As described above, motor control is regulated by nuclei in the basal ganglia and midbrain. Various nuclei in the medulla modulate autonomic functions like breathing and heart rate. In addition, nerves from the brainstem coordinate with the cortex to control the body's state of consciousness and sleep. In summary, the brainstem assists in regulating and controlling swallowing, heart rate, hearing, breathing, blood pressure, balance, and facial sensations.

Damage to the brainstem can result in various neurological disorders such as stroke, multiple sclerosis, and parkinsonism.

THE CEREBRUM, CEREBELLUM, AND BRAINSTEM

The Cerebrum

Cerebral Hemispheres

The cerebrum is a large part of the brain that is responsible for regulating body temperature, controlling movement, facilitating sensory functions (vision, touch, hearing, smell, and taste), enabling speech, and managing emotions and behaviour. It is also considered the "seat of higher consciousness." Often, the term cerebrum is used to describe the entire brain, mainly because it makes up 85% of the brain.

The cerebrum is the main portion of the brain that is divided into the right and left cerebral hemispheres. Each hemisphere is responsible for dominant behaviors and functions, but they work together and communicate through a network of nerve fibers. For example, the left hemisphere functions predominantly on language, mathematics, and logic, while the right hemisphere is responsible for visual imagery, musical abilities, facial recognition, and spatial capabilities. In addition, each side of the cerebrum operates and controls the opposite side of the body. The longitudinal fissure is a deep groove that separates the cerebral hemispheres. The corpus callosum is an arching structure of white matter that connects the two hemispheres at the centre of the cerebrum and allows them to communicate with one another.

The outermost area of the cerebrum is made up of the cerebral cortex, also called "gray matter," a 0.1-inch thick sheet of millions of glial cells and neurons. Beneath the cerebral cortex or gray matter is the "white matter," which is a mass of neurons connected to one another by myelinated fibers that carry electrical impulses to and from the cortex. The surface of the cerebral cortex consists of ridges, folds, and grooves, which give the brain its "wrinkled" appearance. Smaller grooves on the brain's surface are called sulci, the larger grooves are called fissures, and the ridges between the grooves are called gyri. The folds and furrows of the cortex provide important "landmarks" for various anatomical features of the brain. The cerebral cortex's fissures and sulci divide the hemispheres into broad areas of the brain called lobes. There are four pairs of lobes, namely the frontal, temporal, occipital, and parietal lobes.

The Four Lobes of the Cerebrum

The four lobes of the cerebrum are responsible for specific cognitive, motor, and sensory functions in the body, but work in close coordination with one another to regulate behavior. They are classified according to the bones of the skull that cover them.

1. *Frontal lobes:* This area is involved in higher-order cognitive functions like personality, social behavior, planning, decision-making, problem-solving, and voluntary movements. There are sections in the frontal lobes also responsible for smell and speech. Other functions of the frontal lobes are judgement, emotions, intelligence, self-awareness, concentration, and body movement.

2. *Temporal lobes:* These lobes contain various structures like the amygdala and hippocampus that are involved in cognitive functions like language comprehension, the formation of memory, emotions, social cognition, and auditory processing. Other functions of the temporal lobes are regulating speech, smell recognition, short-term memory, hearing, and organization.

3. *Occipital lobes:* The occipital lobes control aspects of vision like movement, color, and light. They also receive stimuli from the visual system to process shapes, object recognition, and visual perception.

4. *Parietal lobes:* This area of the cerebrum is primarily responsible for processing spatial awareness and other sensory information. It allows the identification of objects and the body's position in relation to those objects. It also processes language and words, interprets touch, temperature, and pain, and processes visual, auditory,

motor, sensory, and memory information and stimuli. Further, the parietal lobes use proprioceptors in the muscles to create awareness of body position.

Both the left and right cerebral hemispheres have one of the four lobes, all of which function together in a series of complex patterns. The frontal and parietal lobes of each hemisphere are separated from one another by the central sulcus, while the temporal lobe is separated from the parietal lobe by the lateral sulcus. The parieto-occipital succus divides the parietal lobe from the occipital lobe. Because the four lobes of the cerebrum work in conjunction with one another to regulate movement, behavior, cognition, and perception, any damage to one or more of these lobes can result in disability of the actual function of the lobes as well as corresponding functions.

The four lobes of the cerebrum are discussed in greater detail in Chapter 4.

The Cerebellum

Structure and Function

Located just behind the brainstem beneath the occipital lobes and within the posterior cranial fossa, the cerebellum is responsible for motor skills like balance, coordination, and movement. While the cerebrum manages fine movement control, the cerebellum focuses on major muscle movement and maintains posture. Also called the "little brain," the cerebellum has two hemispheres and is also responsible for maintaining balance and equilibrium by coordinating voluntary muscle movements. The cerebellum also controls and manages various cognitive functions and responses like language, fear, pleasure, and attention. The cerebrum and cerebellum are separated from one another by a tough fold of dura mater, also called the tentorium cerebelli.

The cerebellum consists of two lateral hemispheres, each made up of three lobes, namely the anterior, posterior, and flocculonodular lobes. These lobes are connected to one another by another lobe called the vermis. Much like other sections of the brain, the cerebellum has an outer layer of cortical matter or gray matter made up of neurons, and an internal layer of white matter that maintains communication with the outer layer. Because the white matter of the cerebellum forms a branch-like structure, it is also referred to as the "tree of life" or arbor vitae. Various folds and fissures in the surface of the cerebellum have led it to be likened to that of a cauliflower. The cerebellum is so finely packed with nerves that although it is only 10% of the brain's weight, it contains almost 80% of the brain's neurons.

The cerebellum has three main functions:

1. *Motor control and learning:* allowing motor skills to be refined through practice by guiding and adapting motor control.
2. *Balance:* coordinating various signals and stimuli related to the position and movement of the body to maintain balance.
3. *Movement coordination:* adjusting muscle movement and activity as a result of signals received from sensory systems like proprioceptors in the muscles, and the visual, auditory, and vestibular systems.

New research suggests that the cerebellum may also be involved in regulating social behavior and other cognitive functions related to motor control. It is also thought that the cerebellum is associated with language, although this function is not yet fully understood.

Damage to the cerebellum can result in conditions known as ataxia, which is the loss of muscle control, balance, and issues with walking. Symptoms of ataxia include difficulty swallowing, problems with motor and muscle control, blurry vision, loss of coordination, slurred speech, and headaches. There are several disorders that affect the cerebellum to cause ataxia, for example, stroke, tumors, cerebral palsy, viral infections, and head trauma.

Motor Coordination and Balance

The cerebellum can be divided into different sections based on their functions. There are three main functional divisions, namely the cerebrocerebellum, the spinocerebellum, and the vestibularcerebellum. The cerebrocerebellum is responsible for motor learning, muscle activation, and movements guided by vision. It also contributes to any cognitive functions facilitated in the cerebellum. The spinocerebellum coordinates body movements based on signals received from the proprioceptors in the muscles and is responsible for motor coordination. The vestibulocerebellum takes information from the vestibular system to control movements or balance and maintain posture.

The cerebral cortex (gray matter) of the vermis, which is the central cerebellar zone, is responsible for coordinating movement of the the the neck, shoulders, abdomen, and hips. Alongside the vermis, the intermediate cerebellar zone controls any movement of the muscles of the distal extremity, namely lower arms, legs, hands, and feet. Any coordinated movements involving all muscles of the body are regulated by the lateral areas of each hemisphere of the cerebellum.

Balance in the body is controlled via stimuli received from various receptors such as proprioreceptors and vestibular receptors. The cerebellum takes this information and adjusts the body's posture to maintain balance. This is done by controlling the commands that are received by motor neurons to regulate changes in the body's position or the loads received by muscles.

Any voluntary movement in the body is a result of the coordination of various muscles working together. This coordinated movement is controlled by the cerebellum, which times muscle activation to allow for smooth actions in the body or limbs.

The coordinated activation of several muscles in the body to maintain balance, control, posture, and stability is a complex process that involves precise timing and compensation. For example, when walking, the body needs to maintain posture, balance, and coordination to prevent one from falling over. The cerebellum uses stimuli received from receptors in the body and limbs to interpret information about the body's movement and position in the environment. It then uses this information to plan and time how to activate various muscles to perform the required forward movement. While this is happening, the cerebellum keeps track of the body and its position to modify and adjust muscle activities to retain balance. In addition, the cerebellum coordinates the movement of the lower limbs and body involved in walking, with the muscles of the upper body that contribute to the activity, like the arms and the trunk, to retain stability and balance.

Brainstem Functions

The brainstem, which is located at the base of the brain in front of the cerebellum, is connected to the spinal cord and is composed of three main elements. The brainstem functions as a relay station between the brain and the rest of the body, transmitting various signals and information that allow the body to function and survive effectively. The three main sections of the brainstem are:

1. *Medulla oblongata:* Found between the pons and the spinal cord, the medulla oblongata is responsible for regulating various essential autonomic functions such as breathing, digestion, blood pressure, and heart rate. It also controls reflexive bodily functions like sneezing, swallowing, and coughing. Any significant damage to the medulla oblongata can result in a patient being declared "brain dead," as it controls all the functions of the body necessary for survival.
2. *Pons:* The pons is responsible for controlling facial and eye movements and processes all stimuli received by the facial nerves. The word pons means "bridge," which describes the fiber tracts that connect the midbrain to the medulla. The pons is also the location of the origin of several cranial nerves.
3. *The midbrain:* Also called the mesocephalon, this area connects the pons to the dinocephalon and acts to transfer

various motor signals. It is also responsible for processing both visual and auditory information. The structure responsible for releasing dopamine and controlling movement and coordination, called the substantia nigra, is also found in the midbrain.

The fourth section of the brainstem, the diencephalon, is divided further into four elements namely the hypothalamus, subthalamus, thalamus, and epithalamus. These sections are discussed in greater detail in Chapter 7.

Respiratory Control

Control and regulation of breathing is crucial to regulate the required depth and frequency of respiration needed to support metabolic functions. In addition, the brain needs to integrate various stimuli to ensure that body movement and posture is coordinated with ventilation. Further to this, the effective functioning of the respiratory system is closely linked to emotions and the circulation of blood through the body to oxygenate and supply nutrients to cell tissues. Respiratory control is modulated by several regions of the brain, specifically within the medulla oblongata and pons of the brainstem, as well as the amygdala and hypothalamus of the limbic system. Recent research also suggests that the cerebellum may be indirectly involved in respiration by coordinating the muscles required for breathing to maintain stability and posture. Studies show that the cerebellum is activated during periods of labored breathing, such as hypoxia, or during slow breathing, while also being significantly impacted by changes in environmental air pressure (Krohn et al., 2023).

Respiratory control systems in the brainstem regulate ventilation in the alveoli of the lungs to control the concentration of both arterial oxygen and carbon dioxide. The hypothalamus and amygdala control and regulate involuntary or subconscious breathing. The amygdala is activated under emotional states of fear, as a result of rapid breathing induced by carbon dioxide increases in the bloodstream. In stressful situations that trigger hypoxia (a decreased level of oxygen in the blood), the hypothalamus mediates respiration to decrease heart rate and increase blood pressure.

The superior region of the pons in the brainstem holds the pneumatoxic center, which controls the timing and duration of respiratory cycles by regulating the periods between exhalation and inhalation, as well as the pattern and depth of respiration. Also located within the brainstem, the medulla oblongata is the center of respiratory control. There are two respiratory groups, the ventral respiratory group (VRG) and the dorsal respiratory group (DRG) that are responsible for managing respiration. The VRG mainly controls expiratory muscles, especially when the demand on the respiratory system is high, but does work on both inspiratory and expiratory (breathing out) functions. The DRG initiates inspiratory movements (breathing in) and general respiration rhythms.

In addition to respiratory control systems in the pons and medulla oblongata, there is evidence to suggest that the cerebral cortex is also responsible for normal respiration rhythms during periods of wakefulness. Specifically, this refers to voluntary breathing patterns required during activities such as singing, speaking, or breath-holding; here, the involuntary breathing system can be overridden.

Sleep Regulation

The regulation of periods of sleep and wakefulness is mainly controlled by six regions of the brain: the thalamus, the brainstem, the basal forebrain, the hypothalamus, the pineal gland, and the cortex. The thalamus is the relay station for sensory information that prompts the transitions between sleeping and waking. It moves stimuli from various sensory receptors in the body to the cerebral cortex, which processes the required activity patterns. The thalamus also sends information to the cortex during periods of dreaming.

Sleep-wake transitions are also controlled by the brainstem, which sends signals to the hypothalamus to produce a neurotransmitter called gamma-aminobutyric acid (GABA) that decreases levels of arousal to promote sleep. Also in the brainstem, the pons and the medulla work to relax body muscles during rapid eye movement (REM) sleep to prevent movement during dreaming.

The basal forebrain produces essential neurotransmitters like adenosine that encourage relaxation, suppress arousal, and promote the transition from wakefulness to sleep. It also releases the chemical acetylcholine, an excitatory neurotransmitter that increases during periods of REM and promotes various sleep stages.

As mentioned above, the hypothalamus secretes GABA, as well as melanin-concentrating hormone (MCH), which are neurotransmitters that promote sleep. The hypothalamus contains a group of cells called the suprachiasmatic nucleus (SCN) that receive and process light stimuli through the eyes to regulate the sleep-wake cycle or circadian rhythm. The SCN is also called the "body clock" as a result of its role in regulating sleeping patterns.

A pea-sized endocrine gland located behind the thalamus, the pineal gland, secretes melatonin, which is a hormone responsible for encouraging sleep during periods of low light and darkness. The release of melatonin is prompted by sensory signals received by the SCN.

While the cerebral cortex is not directly responsible for regulating the sleep-wake cycle or promoting sleep, patterns of activity in this region decrease significantly during periods of sleep. This reduces any response to and awareness of external information received during sleep.

Cranial Nerves and Sensory Pathways

There are twelve cranial nerves, each responsible for various activities within the upper body, including the neck and head. Each cranial nerve has its origin in the brain and is composed of brainstem nuclei and cortical structures, as opposed to spinal nerves that emerge from the spinal cortex. The cranial nerves can be divided into three groups according to their functions, namely sensory, motor, or both. Cranial nerves contribute to various motor and sensory activities and functions such as balance, swallowing, vision, smell, taste, hearing, and facial movements.

Cranial nerves are numbered and named anatomically according to the sequence in which they emerge from the cranium, their location on the brainstem, and their function:

I- Olfactory

The olfactory nerve functions in a sensory capacity and regulates the sense of smell.

II- Optic

The optic nerve is also sensory and is responsible for vision.

III- Oculomotor

The third cranial nerve is both sensory and motor and controls eye movement, pupillary reflex, and eyelid position.

IV- Trochlear

The trochlear nerve is a motor nerve that plays a role in the upward and inward movement of the eyes, innervating the superior oblique muscle of the eye.

V- Trigeminal

There are three main branches to the trigeminal nerve, namely the ophthalmic, maxillary, and mandibular branches. This motor nerve controls muscles of the jaw and face for chewing and provides nerves to the face, teeth, and scalp.

VI- Abducens

The abducens nerve has a motor function to control the muscle that moves the eye in an outwards motion. This muscle is called the lateral rectus.

VII- Facial

The facial nerve has mixed functions (motor and sensory) and innervates the face for facial expressions, as well as the production of tears and saliva. It is also involved in taste.

VIII- Vestibulocochlear

This sensory nerve is involved in hearing and balance and has two branches, namely the vestibular nerve (balance) and the cochlear nerve (hearing).

IX- Glossopharyngeal

The glossopharyngeal nerve has both sensory and motor functions. It functions to monitor blood pressure and arterial oxygen concentrations. It also works to control voluntary speech and swallowing actions and is involved in taste, too.

X- Vagus

The vagus nerve has sensory and motor functions and controls throat and neck muscles for reflex actions such as swallowing, sneezing, and coughing. It also regulates various abdominal organs for digestion and breathing.

XI- Spinal accessory

This motor nerve stimulates movement in the shoulders, neck, and head, such as rotation, tilting, and flexing. It also contributes to activities in the larynx.

XII- Hypoglossal

The last cranial nerve has motor functions to control tongue muscles for speaking, movement of the food during chewing, and swallowing.

DISORDERS OF THE BRAIN

Brain disorders can be divided into two main categories, neurological and psychiatric. Neurological disorders include all illnesses and diseases that affect both the central and peripheral nervous systems. This can include brain tumors, traumatic brain injuries, epilepsy, multiple sclerosis, Alzheimer's and Parkinson's disease, migraines, and infections of the nervous system. Psychiatric disorders, also sometimes referred to as mental illnesses, are illnesses that affect how the brain functions and cause disturbances in emotions, behavior, and moods. Examples of psychiatric disorders include depression, bipolar disorder, schizophrenia, anxiety, and dissociative disorders.

Neurological Disorders

Neurological disorders are caused by infection by viruses and bacteria. The symptoms of a neurological illness as a result of infection can either be the nervous system's immune response to the infection or the infection itself. These symptoms can vary depending on the illness but include problems with memory, learning, breathing, movement, speech, mood, and sensations. Neurological disorders can be caused by genetics, infections, injury to the brain, or abnormalities that occur in a fetus before birth (congenital).

Stroke

Medically, and most commonly, a stroke occurs when the supply of blood to the brain is cut off. Without a sufficient supply of blood, brain cells don't receive enough oxygen and nutrients to function. If blood supply remains interrupted, brain cells may start dying. The symptoms of a stroke are dependent on the region of the brain that is affected by the lack of blood supply, as well as the extent of the damage. Strokes can also be caused by bleeding on the brain.

There are three main types of stroke, namely ischaemic, hemorrhagic, and transient ischaemic:

1. *Ischaemic stroke:* Most strokes are ischaemic. This occurs when the blood supply to the brain is blocked, damaging or killing brain cells. Generally, ischaemic strokes are caused by the narrowing of the blood vessels that carry blood from the heart to the brain. However, they can also be caused by the narrowing of blood vessels in the brain, irregular heartbeats, and damage to the lining of large arteries.

2. *Haemorrhagic stroke:* A hemorrhagic stroke is caused by bleeding on or around the brain. This occurs when blood vessels in the brain rupture. As with an ischaemic stroke, bleeding on the brain prevents essential oxygen and nutrients from reaching brain cells, damaging or killing them. The main symptom of a hemorrhagic stroke is the sudden onset of a severe headache. Hemorrhagic strokes can be caused by head trauma, infections in the brain, aneurysms (the ballooning of an arterial wall due to the weakening of the artery), bleeding tumors, or damaged blood vessels.

3. *Transient ischaemic stroke:* The transient ischaemic stroke (TIA) is often considered to be a warning sign of an impending stroke. Because of this, it is also referred to as a mini-stroke. Similarly to ischaemic strokes, TIA occurs as a result of a disruption in the brain's blood supply. Although the symptoms of a TIA are similar to other types of strokes, it doesn't last as long as an ischaemic stroke. Generally, the symptoms of a TIA may disappear after an hour.

Strokes occur suddenly and someone suffering from a stroke may become confused and disoriented. They may be unable to speak or understand their surroundings and may experience a severe headache. Strokes also cause dizziness, a loss of balance, and paralysis of the face and limbs, usually on one side of the body only.

Strokes can affect people of all ages. However, there is a cluster of underlying conditions that can increase the risk of stroke. These include high cholesterol, diabetes, high blood pressure, genetics, and atrial fibrillation (a medical condition causing an irregular heart rate). Certain lifestyle habits can also increase the possibility of a stroke occurring, such as smoking, excessive alcohol consumption, obesity, and a fatty or unhealthy diet.

Epilepsy

Epilepsy is identified by the onset of seizures. A seizure occurs when the brain experiences a sudden surge of excessive electrical activity. This abnormal burst in electrical stimuli can lead to changes in behavior and awareness and may cause involuntary functions or movements. While normal brains have the potential to experience a seizure, people with epilepsy have a much lower threshold for these seizures, which means they tend to happen more frequently. It can be challenging to identify the specific cause of the onset of seizures in a person with epilepsy, but they may be triggered by infections of the brain, brain tumors, stroke, traumatic head injuries, or birth asphyxia (a lack of sufficient oxygen at birth).

A person with epilepsy is more likely to experience unprovoked and recurring seizures. There are two main types of seizures, namely generalized onset seizures and focal onset seizures. Generalized seizures are characterized by attacks that affect both sides of the brain and result in impaired awareness. Within the category of generalized seizures, one may experience absence seizures, which may cause rapid blinking or prolonged staring. Also a generalized form of seizure, tonic-clonic seizures cause muscle spasms, falling, and a loss of consciousness.

Focal onset seizures are so called because they may either start on one side of the brain, or within a group of cells on one side of the brain. Someone experiencing a focal onset seizure may have their awareness impaired, as with generalized seizures, or can be fully aware. If a seizure spreads from one side of the brain to the other, it can turn into a tonic-clonic seizure. This is also referred to as a secondary generalized seizure. Focal onset seizures can cause twitching, confusion, disorientation, or unusual tastes and smells.

Multiple Sclerosis

Multiple sclerosis (MS) is a neurological disorder whereby the fatty and protective myelin sheaths that surround neurons in the central nervous system become damaged. If myelin is damaged, neurons are ineffective at transferring electrical stimuli through the neural circuits, and messages become disrupted.

Damage to the myelin sheath of neurons occurs when the body's immune system becomes overactive. It then starts mistaking myelin cells for foreign or harmful substances and attacks them. This process is referred to as demyelination. While scientists are not fully certain of what causes the onset of MS, it is believed to be potentially triggered by exposure to toxins, smoking, childhood obesity, and genetics.

Multiple sclerosis is divided into four main categories based on the patient's symptoms. Clinically isolated syndrome (CIS) refers to a patient who exhibits the early symptoms of MS but does not clinically have MS. Relapsing-remitting multiple sclerosis (RRMS) occurs when a patient experiences remission of symptoms interspersed between flare-ups or attacks of MS. Secondary progressive multiple sclerosis (SPMS) refers to the worsening of symptoms experienced by someone with RRMS. Primary progressive multiple sclerosis (PPMS) occurs when MS symptoms get progressively worse over time and the patient does not experience any remission.

Symptoms of MS include changes in mood, loss of coordination and balance, issues with thinking, memory, and learning, muscle tremors and stiffness, dizziness, fatigue, and clumsiness.

Alzheimer's Disease

Alzheimer's disease is the most common form of dementia, making up more than 70% of dementia disorders. Because it is more likely to occur in people over the age of 65 years, it is also referred to as an age-related disease. Alzheimer's is a progressive disease, which means the symptoms of dementia get worse over time. This neurological disorder causes disruptions in thinking, mood, behavior, learning, and memory. One of the primary symptoms of Alzheimer's is the inability to remember newly acquired information. This is because Alzheimer's affects the parts of the brain that are responsible for cognitive processes like thinking, learning, and memory.

As the disease progresses, people with Alzheimer's begin to show worsening symptoms. This can include increasing confusion about events and places, paranoia and suspicion about those around them, behavior changes, difficulty swallowing, disorientation, and changes in mood.

The exact cause of Alzheimer's and its progressive symptoms are still unclear. However, neurologists believe that the damage to neurons can start long before the sufferer starts showing symptoms. Currently, theories suggest that the abnormal deposition of plaque in the brain can cause blockages in information transmission between neurons. Research shows that people with Alzheimer's have a greater quantity of plaque buildup than those without. Plaque is a build-up of a type of protein called beta-amyloid in between neurons. Besides preventing the movement of signals along neural pathways, plaque can also block essential metabolic processes the nerve cells need to survive. This degeneration and death of neurons in someone with Alzheimer's is what causes symptoms like memory loss, poor judgment, increased anxiety, and confusion.

Psychiatric Disorders

Generally, psychiatric disorders are diagnosed if the symptoms expressed prevent a person from exhibiting normal behavior and are more severe than those expected after a trauma or loss. The National Institute of Mental Health (NIMH) reports that more than five percent of U.S. adults experience serious mental illness (Salters-Pedneault, 2023). Psychiatric disorders can present a variety of symptoms, including deep feelings of sadness, extreme tiredness, paranoia, detachment, excessive anger, rapid mood changes, withdrawal from daily life, confusion, and more seriously, suicidal thoughts.

Depression

Also known as depressive disorders, depression is categorized by extreme feelings of sadness, hopelessness, and worthlessness. Depressive disorders can be divided into several types, namely major depressive disorder, persistent depressive disorder, premenstrual dysphoric disorder, perinatal depression, seasonal affective disorder, and depression with psychosis. Depression is also sometimes referred to as major depressive disorder (MDD).

For someone to be diagnosed with a depressive disorder, they need to be experiencing various symptoms for more than two weeks, with a disruption in normal behavior and functioning. Symptoms of depression can be mild or severe and include loss of interest in previously enjoyable activities, weight loss or gain, changes in sleeping patterns, feelings of guilt, difficulty making decisions, and suicidal ideation. Besides causing changes in mood and daily patterns of activity, depression can cause behavioral changes like an increase in impulsivity, increased substance abuse, increased irritability, and isolation from loved ones.

Depression can have multiple causes, from environmental factors like domestic abuse or trauma, violence, and poverty, to physiological factors like genetics and changes in brain chemistry. Scientists also suggest that people with a more pessimistic outlook on life are more prone to periods of depression.

It is important to note that depression, while often triggered by a traumatic life event, is different from feelings of grief or sadness. Depression can be treated with a combination of medication, psychotherapy, and changes in lifestyle.

Schizophrenia

Schizophrenia is a form of psychotic disorder, which manifest as psychosis. Psychoses cause delusional thinking, detachment from reality, abnormal behavior, disordered speaking and thinking, and auditory and visual hallucinations. Someone with schizophrenia will experience episodes of psychosis.

Clinical symptoms of schizophrenia can be categorized as positive or negative; however, this does not explain whether a symptom is good or bad. Rather, positive symptoms are only present in someone with schizophrenia, while negative symptoms are those present in 'healthier' individuals that disappear or become reduced in someone experiencing a psychotic episode.

Examples of positive schizophrenic symptoms include delusions, hallucinations, disorganized speech, and disorganized behaviour. Delusions are distorted, false beliefs that the sufferer believes to be true, regardless of rationality. Negative symptoms are anhedonia, which is a decreased sense of enjoyment of things that usually bring pleasure; reduced speech, which is a decrease in the amount of speaking compared to normal; and a lack of initiative, where the sufferer experiences a loss of will to do something, and is similar to avolition, which is a loss of motivation.

In addition to clinical symptoms, people with schizophrenia also exhibit cognitive symptoms, which affect the way a person thinks. Examples of cognitive symptoms in someone with schizophrenia include problems with working memory, lack of insight into their illness, an inability to focus, and difficulty planning ahead.

People with schizophrenia may also display symptoms of other psychiatric disorders like anxiety, depression, anger, substance abuse, and disrupted sleep patterns.

Anxiety Disorders

Anxiety disorders refer to psychiatric conditions whereby people experience fearful and negative thought patterns and express excessive concern over potentially bad, harmful, or dangerous future events. This fear is in anticipation of what may happen, whether real or not. Mild anxiety is normal and can be helpful in everyday life to prevent harm and injury; however, anxiety disorders are more related to avoidance of perceived future threats and may include associated physical symptoms like muscle tension. Up to 30% of adults may experience anxiety disorders (*What are anxiety disorders?*, n.d., para. 1). Anxiety disorders are diagnosed when feelings of fear or anxiety are out of proportion to the event, object, or activity, or if the reaction to these is not appropriate to the age of the sufferer. Anxiety disorders can also inhibit a person's ability to function normally. There are three main categories of anxiety disorders:

1. *Generalized anxiety disorder (GAD):* characterized by excessive anxiety over a wide range of issues. People with GAD often suffer co-occurring psychiatric disorders like depression and substance abuse. They are unable to control their concerns and may experience physical symptoms such as fatigue, insomnia, irritability, headaches, stomachaches, and muscle tension.
2. *Panic disorder:* This is characterized by frequent, recurrent, severe, and unexpected panic attacks. Symptoms of a panic attack include heart palpitations, sweating, shaking, nausea, shortness of breath, chest pain, and fear of dying, going crazy, or losing control.
3. *Phobias:* Phobias are identified as excessive worry and concern over specific activities, events, or objects. Intense distress and even panic attacks are triggered by these concerns. This leads sufferers to avoid the feared object, event, or activity and can disrupt normal day-to-day functioning. Examples include social phobia (excessive fear of social situations), agoraphobia (excessive fear of anxiety, helplessness, or feelings of being trapped), and acrophobia (an intense fear of heights).

Bipolar Disorders

Bipolar disorder is characterized by rapid and sudden shifts in mood, levels of activity, sleep patterns, and energy. These "mood episodes," which are distinct periods of either mania or depression, can last from a few days to several weeks. Mood episodes are very different from the person's usual behavior, and generally sufferers are unable to recognize these changes in behavior and mood, even if they are harmful.

Mood episodes can be manic, depressive, or a combination of both (an episode with mixed features). Manic episodes are recognized by feelings of extreme irritability, racing thoughts, ability to function for longer periods with little or no sleep, feelings of grandiosity, feeling jumpy, experiencing euphoria, impulsivity, difficulty focusing, or experiencing an elevated need for pleasurable activities like food, drinking, or gambling. Alternately, depressive episodes manifest as periods of listlessness, feelings of excessive guilt or worthlessness, loss of previously enjoyable activities, fatigue, loss of energy, changes in sleeping patterns, and recurrent thoughts of suicide.

There are three main types of bipolar disorder:

1. *Bipolar I disorder:* experiencing manic episodes that last almost all day, every day for at least seven days. May include depressive periods of at least two weeks. Manic episodes may be so severe that the sufferer requires medical care.
2. *Bipolar II disorder:* experiencing cycles of both depressive and hypomanic episodes. Hypomanic episodes are a milder form of mania and don't often require medical care.
3. *Cyclothymic disorder:* experiencing recurring symptoms of hypomania and depression. However, these periods are not severe or extensive enough to be classified as hypomanic or depressive episodes.

BRAIN PLASTICITY AND ADAPTATION

Neuroplasticity

Definition and Mechanisms

Plasticity refers to an organism's adaptability, or its ability to change. In neuroscience, the plasticity of the brain and nervous system is called neuroplasticity. Neuroplasticity is scientifically defined as "the ability of the nervous system to change its activity in response to intrinsic or extrinsic stimuli by reorganizing its structure, functions, or connections after injuries, such as a stroke or traumatic brain injury" (Puderbaugh & Emmady, 2023, para. 3). In other words, the brain and nervous system can change and adapt, both structurally and functionally, to experiences, injury, and environmental effects. Neuroplasticity allows the brain to prune damaged or unused synapses, form new synaptic connections, and strengthen existing ones.

One of the most significant examples of neuroplasticity is the change that occurs in a person's brain structure and function as they grow and develop through life. The brain continues to adapt, grow, and reorganize from birth, through adulthood, and into old age. However, the brain's neuroplasticity does decline as a person ages. The ability of a brain to change and adapt allows functional and structural responses to experiences, regeneration after injury or trauma, and adaptability to new experiences.

There are two main mechanisms, or systems, which occur in neuro-plasticity to bring about change and reorganization of the brain. These are functional reorganization or plasticity, and neuronal regeneration (also known as structural plasticity).

1. *Functional reorganization:* This refers to changes in neurons. Undamaged areas of the brain also can take over from or compensate for areas that have been damaged, so that it can continue to work effectively.

2. *Structural plasticity:* This refers to the brain's ability to change structurally and includes the growth of new connections between dendrites and axons, as well as the formation of new synapses.

There are various ways to encourage the brain's neuroplasticity. These include introducing new and unique experiences, practicing established patterns and activities, resting sufficiently, exercising, and stimulating the brain with brain games and enrichment. The more frequently a neuronal circuit is used, the stronger it will become. In the same way, rarely used neurons will die and be removed.

There are several benefits to neuroplasticity (Cherry, 2022):

- boosting the brain's fitness, which is its ability to work efficiently
- strengthening areas of the brain where functions have declined or been lost
- enhancing existing cognitive abilities
- learning new things
- recovery from brain illness or trauma

While neuroplasticity is mostly seen as a positive mechanism, there can be challenges with certain changes that can occur in the brain. In some cases, the effects of substance abuse, trauma (physical or emotional), and disease can be worsened by the brain's ability to adapt and change. The brain has a unique ability to adapt to learning, new experiences, environmental changes, trauma, and illness. While this potential for change is extensive, there are areas of the brain, that when damaged, are unable to fully revert to their original functions.

Role in Recovery and Learning

Damage to the brain can be a result of physical or emotional trauma. For example, a traumatic experience can result in a jump in the brain's "fight-or-flight" response, in which the amygdala is excessively triggered. A hyperactive amygdala causes exaggerated responses to subsequent events and experiences, even if they are not threatening. This can lead to the development of a condition called post-traumatic stress disorder (PTSD). In PTSD, a sense of danger, anger, fear, or rage can be triggered by certain stimuli related to the actual trauma. While PTSD is not formally considered a traumatic brain injury (TBI), the structural and functional effects on the brain are similar to those caused by a physical injury. Excessive physical force to the skull can result in a TBI and damage to the brain. Symptoms of physical and psychological trauma are similar to one another and can include loss of motor control, depression, anxiety, irritability, mood swings, and confusion.

Trauma can affect various areas of the brain in different ways. Trauma to the amygdala causes heightened emotions and may lead to anxiety disorders. Damage to the hippocampus, which controls memory, can cause problems with learning and memory. If the prefrontal cortex (PFC) is damaged, the patient may experience issues with impulse control, decision-making, and planning. Trauma to the PFC can also increase the probability of the patient developing PTSD. Damage to the basal ganglia leads to issues with basic functions like breathing, blood pressure, and heart rate.

The ability of the brain to adapt and change plays a critical role in its effective recovery from trauma, disease, or illness. The brain's functional plasticity mechanism is important for recovery from injury. When the brain is exposed to illness or trauma, it may stop functioning the way it should, affecting its cognitive and motor abilities. The ability of a brain to recover from injury or illness is largely a result of the dynamic properties of synaptic connections. For example, when someone suffers from a stroke, which is caused by a blood clot or hemorrhage in the brain, the delivery of oxygen in the bloodstream is reduced, causing nerve cells to die off. Depending on the area of the brain that is affected, the patient may experience a loss of motor control or speech. The brain's malleable characteristics allow for the automatic rewiring of neuronal pathways and the formation of new synapses in the event of damage such as this.

Patients undergoing rehabilitation from substance abuse also benefit greatly from neuroplasticity. When exposed to certain addictive substances in narcotics and alcohol, the brain's chemistry is altered, causing damage to neurons. Understanding the mechanism of neuroplasticity is vital in addressing various neurological and psychiatric disorders and recovery from trauma, and offers insight into processes of learning and memory. The brain's ability to adapt and regrow in response to trauma allows it to heal itself and regain previously lost motor, cognitive, and emotional functions.

Rehabilitation and Brain Adaptation

Post-Injury Recovery

Traumatic brain injury can present with a variety of symptoms, including poor concentration, loss of coordination, confusion, slurred speech, dizziness, issues with memory, and personality changes. Post-injury therapy is essential to regenerate the damaged areas of the brain and restore impaired motor and cognitive functions. Effective therapy and recovery can prevent indirect complications from TBI, which can include various physical dysfunctions like muscle weakness, pneumonia, blood clots, and pain.

Rehabilitation of the brain, which is the process of recovery or restoration after an injury or illness, is enhanced by neuroplasticity. During rehabilitation, the brain's ability to adapt and change is harnessed to promote its recovery from structural or functional damage. By reorganizing neuronal patterns and encouraging new synaptic connections, the brain can relearn lost skills and achieve recovery. This is significantly illustrated in the common ability of stroke patients to regain lost motor and physical control, and skills through practiced activities. Stroke patients undergo intensive rehabilitation, where they are encouraged to visualize their ability to complete certain tasks, even if the physical control is not available. This is called motor imagery. By imagining their completion of activities and tasks, neuroscientists believe that stroke patients activate those neural circuits in the brain, rebuilding and strengthening synaptic connections. Stroke patients also engage in repetitive, intense physical exercises and drills to promote the regrowth and strengthening of damaged synaptic connections.

There are three phases to the recovery of neurons after trauma or illness. The first phase occurs shortly after the injury with the death of brain cells. This occurs for several days, during which time new or secondary nerve pathways are exposed. Following that, the second phase involves prolific synaptogenesis, or the formation of new synaptic connections, and neurogenesis (neuronal proliferation), which is the generation of new neurons. The third phase, which occurs several weeks post-injury, sees the remodeling of the damaged sections of the brain with the increased sprouting of new synapses. This induces recovery.

It is important to start trauma recovery immediately following a brain injury or trauma. Extensive rehabilitation can prove incredibly successful in recovery and can promote quality of life in patients.

Training-Induced Changes in the Brain

Repetitive task training (RTT) and movement therapy are two examples of recovery and rehabilitation techniques used to speed up healing after brain trauma (Zotey et al. 2023). In RTT, the patient is encouraged to consistently repeat various physical exercises and motor functions to promote the regrowth of synaptic connections. In constraint-induced movement therapy (CIMT), the patient is required to use the affected limb while the movement of the unaffected limb is restricted. This forces the reorganization and regeneration of damaged synapses. In physical therapy (PT) a patient engages in recurrent and intense task-specific drills that mimic real functions. Because the patient is re-enacting familiar exercises, the brain uses past experiences to re-wire damaged neural pathways. Often, CIMT is used in conjunction with PT to stimulate affected parts of the body for rapid recovery and healing.

Another effective method of managing and healing brain injuries and trauma is through speech and language therapy. This is especially effective for injuries that impact the areas of the brain responsible for linguistic and communicative skills (Zotey et al. 2023).

Recovery after a major TBI also relies strongly on developing healthy lifestyle habits and patterns. Repetitive activities and behaviors promote healing by encouraging the rewiring of damaged neuronal networks. Various beneficial routines can be incorporated into daily life to promote healing and recovery:

1. *Exercise:* Regular exercise releases chemicals that reduce feelings of depression, stress, and anxiety, and acts as a mood enhancer. It promotes brain growth and function.
2. *Meditation:* Meditation, which is the act of mindfulness, encourages feelings of calm and peace. This is an ancient practice, scientifically proven to reduce stress, anxiety, and depression, and increase the brain's resilience to trauma.
3. *Mental health:* Engaging in good mental health includes practicing self-awareness and self-care, engaging in therapy, and spending time on enjoyable activities. This can assist in healing and recovery after brain injuries and trauma.
4. *Physical health:* Maintaining good physical health can be done by regularly exercising, healthy eating, good hygiene, and sufficient rest and sleep. This can promote healing and recovery in the brain.

Maintaining good physical and mental health can encourage resilience to trauma. It promotes feelings of well-being and allows one to develop healthy coping mechanisms. It can also encourage the rewiring of damaged or degraded neural pathways to heal dysfunctional processes.

Trauma during the early stages of childhood development can have a significant impact on the brain. This is referred to as childhood trauma and can result in both structural and functional damage. Sufferers may experience issues with stress regulation, emotions, memory, and other cognitive abilities. Prolonged exposure to childhood trauma causes the release of stress hormones, that over time, change important areas of the brain like the hippocampus and amygdala. Children who have experienced early trauma are more likely to develop anxiety and other psychiatric disorders later in life. Fortunately, regular healthy mental and physical practices, as listed above, can assist in the healing of damaged brain structures and function.

FUTURE FRONTIERS IN BRAIN RESEARCH

Emerging Technologies

Brain-Computer Interfaces

A technology that sounds more science-fiction than science, Brain-Computer Interfaces (BCI) aims to allow the user to control devices directly through brain activity. In other words, with BCIs, one can access and control technology with the mind. Generally, if a person wants to exert an action using motor control, the brain and body work together to execute the motion. However, with BCI, computer technology analyzes the information in the brain while it processes the motion and sends a signal to the device or instrument to activate the response. In essence, BCI technology bypasses the muscles of the body and replaces the physical and voluntary reaction to a thought or decision.

Initially, BCIs were developed and designed to assist people with mobility challenges. BCIs can bridge the gap between the brain and muscles to restore any lost motor functions, especially in paralyzed individuals. This allows them to operate and control external systems or robotic devices with their thoughts. However, a surge in research and development into the technology behind BCIs has led to the use of innovation to improve cognitive functions as well. BCIs have also been used to assist those with visual or auditory impairments, chronic pain, and neurological disorders.

There are four main components to a BCI system. Various neurological mapping processes like functional magnetic resonance imagery (fMRI) and electroencephalography (EEG), discussed in Chapter 5, are used to acquire electric signals generated in the brain. From there, these signals are processed to remove noise and ensure information is accurate and reliable. After the brain's activity is processed, features from the signals that are relevant to the task are further extracted and processed. Once the relevant signals are extracted and classified accordingly, the control interface of the BCI system translates the neurological signals from the brain into a control signal. The control signal can then operate an external device according to the user's intention. Lastly, the BCI system provides the user with feedback on the activity of both the brain and the device. This allows the user to operate the system effectively and make sure that the desired action is completed successfully.

Any BCI system requires a device used to measure brain activity like a headband, cap, or headset; computer software to capture, process, and analyze these signals; and a device to control the activity. BCI systems are non-invasive and don't require surgery. They have proven to be successful in assisting those suffering from disorders that impair motor control, like locked-in syndrome, amyotrophic lateral sclerosis (ALS), and other physical disabilities.

Optogenetics

Developed in 2005, optogenetics is a state-of-the-art technology that uses light to activate opsins (light-sensitive pumps in the brain) and manipulate nerve activity. After years of further research, scientists are now able to finely modulate the response time and mode of operation of opsins within milliseconds. In addition, the ability to subtly control the excitation and inhibition of opsins allows scientists to target specialized neurons to address specific neurological disorders like epilepsy, schizophrenia, and Alzheimer's disease. Optogenetics allows neurologists to study, target, and manipulate very specific areas of the brain.

There are two main types of opsins, namely excitatory and inhibitory opsins. Excitatory opsins respond to blue light of wavelengths of approximately 470 nanometres (nm). This is used to depolarize neurons to activate an action potential. On the other hand, inhibitory opsins restrict action potentials from firing under exposure to yellow light ($\approx$580 nm).

Optogenetics harnesses genetic modification to express the ion channels within neurons that are stimulated by light. This is done by triggering ions to move from outside the cell to inside it, causing a neuron to fire. A virus with specifically modified genes is injected into targeted areas of the brain, where it recombines its DNA with that of the brain cells (called host cells). This changes the dynamics required to express the ion channels in those nerve cells, causing an action potential to fire when the threshold is reached on exposure to specific wavelengths of light.

Recently, work has been done by one of the founders of optogenetics to create ion channels sensitive to red light. Red light can penetrate deeper into brain tissue than either blue or yellow light, allowing neuroscientists to reach parts of the brain that have been previously inaccessible.

At this stage, optogenetics is an expensive and complex technique that still requires much research. There is still some uncertainty regarding the long-term effects of this technology, in terms of extensive light exposure and the insertion of foreign genes into the brain. Clinical studies done on non-human mammals have shown that changes to inhibitory ion channels can last longer than the actual photostimulation. However, there is still a lot of research to be done before clinical trials can be started on humans.

Artificial Intelligence in Neurosciences

The relationship between artificial intelligence (AI) and neuroscience is synergetic: While AI is enhancing the field of neuroscience and encouraging breakthroughs in the early diagnosis of psychiatric disorders, neuroscience is responsible for inspiring the architecture behind AI. AI, which is defined as the development of machine learning to stimulate human intelligence, has broadened the scope of neuroscience in recent years by facilitating the rapid analysis of large sets of data.

Data and information generated in the brain are captured by imaging techniques like fMRI and EEG. These extensive data sets can be processed swiftly with the use of AI algorithms, which have the capacity to identify trends in the data that may be too subtle to be recognized by human scientists. For example, illnesses such as meningitis have such a range of symptoms that they are often difficult to diagnose. AI is used to swiftly interpret large data sets and correlations between variables to provide accurate diagnoses, as well as potential options for treatment and recovery.

AI has also contributed to the development of BCIs by bridging the gap between the brain and machines. AI is capable of retrieving neural signals and transmitting them via specific commands to external devices. For example, someone with a paralyzed limb will be able to move a robotic replacement with the help of AI. AI is allowing neuroscientists to study the brain and simulate treatment and interventions without the invasiveness of surgery.

With the help of neuroscientists, AI engineers have used the complex neural circuits in the human brain to recreate similar algorithms for artificial systems. Based on the ability of humans to harness reinforcement learning (enhanced learning based on an immediate reward following an action), computer scientists have "taught" AI machines to perform certain actions without the need for extensive instructions.

Scientists are now exploring methods of further integrating humans and machines to better enhance human cognitive and physical abilities. The idea is to seamlessly facilitate communication between humans and AI systems. However, there are various ethical considerations to keep in mind.

Ethical Considerations

Privacy and Data Security

The recent explosion in AI and machine learning has raised numerous concerns about data security and privacy. Various fears abound, from the loss of control and privacy to the worry that AI will one day take over human-driven jobs. Concerns have arisen over the potential for AI to reach consciousness and surpass human abilities to solve and complete complex tasks. While science has enhanced the ability of neurologists to accurately diagnose and treat various neurological and psychiatric disorders and illnesses, it involves the collection of sensitive data. As AI science advances at a rapid rate, experts stress the importance of protecting privacy and preventing unlawful or unauthorized access to this data.

The regulation of AI-obtained information requires robust and ethical guidelines, protocols, and processes to ensure responsible and safe use. In addition, patients need to be given the chance to express consent for the use of their data by external parties. Because the field is multidisciplinary, it is the responsibility of all involved, including neuroscientists, AI technologists, and policymakers, to develop airtight, ethical frameworks. It is these comprehensive policies and guidelines that will guide users and scientists to ethically and morally implement AI-enhanced neurotechnologies (Balroop, 2023).

The interdisciplinary field of neurotechnology requires responsible use to ensure it can continue advancing to further enhance and improve human intelligence. It offers scientists the chance to better diagnose and treat cognitive disorders and neurological challenges, provided it is used within strict ethical guidelines.

Neuroenhancement and Ethics

Unfortunately, the integration of machine learning with human abilities may provide the opportunity for scientists to blur the line between ethics and accessibility. There is a perceived risk of potential and non-consensual surveillance through AI systems. Concerns have been raised about a loss of value and purpose for humans and their abilities, and the fear that AI will, at some stage, replace humans.

It is essential to uphold ethical principles and promote unbiased use of data. AI-driven technologies should be available across the board to those that need it. It is also important to realize the limit to the capabilities of AI and recognize that, while machine learning has many potential applications to improve the lives of humans, it can never replace humans. AI has been created by humans, to assist humans, and, as long as this is maintained, there should be no threat from machine learning systems. AI technologists suggest, that when navigating the complexity of machine learning, one should always "keep humans in the loop" (Balroop, 2023). This means viewing AI as a tool of assistance and collaborator, rather than a replacement.

When navigating the use of AI to enhance human cognitive processes and address neurological disorders, priority should be given to ethical considerations, as well as societal gains. Any AI-driven neurological enhancement should carefully examine how it contributes to inclusivity and respects individual autonomy (Balroop, 2023).

Brain Manipulation and Moral Dilemmas

Philosophers, psychologists, and anthropologists have long debated the origin of human morality. One of the pervading theories is that morality developed as humans evolved to live in complex, close societies. This was an essential aspect in communities where conflict needed to be managed and resolved to ensure the survival and functioning of the group. While various cultures have slightly different moral codes, most recognize the value of human life, the importance of honesty, and the disapproval of any act that causes harm to others.

As technology progresses at an unprecedented rate, the question of morality in AI and neurological manipulation has emerged as a crucial issue to address. This is an especially significant concern with gene-editing technology, which can alter the DNA of neurons. While this is a prominent advancement in the treatment of genetic brain disorders like Huntington's disease and epilepsy, it also raises the question of the long-term effect of these manipulations. Brain manipulation techniques have also been suggested as a means of enhancing the cognitive abilities of the human brain, such as improving memory, creativity, and intelligence. Again, moral and ethical dilemmas arise in terms of the accessibility of this technology, as well as the limits to its application. Experts have raised concern over 'when enough is enough': At what stage does one restrict brain enhancement, and when does enhancement constitute an unfair advantage over others?

As with many other technologies, there is room for misuse of AI and machine learning. While brain-manipulating techniques such as optogenetics can have life-changing consequences for those suffering from neurological disorders, there is a concern that these advancements can be used for nefarious purposes. Already there has been concern expressed over the recent announcement that scientists have fine-tuned the genetic modification of fetuses to prevent certain illnesses.

Over recent decades, neuroscientists have used science fiction to influence technological progress. Inspired by the potential to adapt and manipulate memories, researchers have developed memory modification techniques (MMT) to modify memory. Originally designed to augment treatment programs for those suffering from addiction, anxiety, PTSD, and memory disorders, MMT has raised various ethical and moral concerns. Experts argue that manipulating and modifying memories may permanently alter one's personality and identity. Again, where does one draw the line between the treatment of neurological and psychiatric disorders, and personal enhancement and gain? Also, the long-term effects of these modifications are not yet clear.

As with anything, there has to be a careful integration of science with ethics and morality, especially when confronted with the infinite possibilities offered by AI.

CONCLUSION

The Journey Through the Brain

Recap of Insights

The human brain is a complex organ, one that neuroscientists are still working to understand. It is the most complicated part of the human body and is considered the source of what it means to be human. Breakthroughs in technology have given deep insight into previously unexplained aspects of the functioning of the brain. While different structures regulate and control various behaviors, emotions, movements, and involuntary actions, it is clear that the brain's components work together to facilitate these functions effectively.

The brain is composed of three main units: the forebrain, midbrain, and hindbrain. The forebrain is the largest and most highly developed region of the brain and controls high-level cognitive processes like sensory processing, emotions, behaviors, motor control, thinking, reasoning, perceptions, memory, and intelligence. It also regulates the body's physiological processes and maintains homeostasis in response to changes in the external environment. It is composed primarily of the cerebrum and structures like the thalamus, hypothalamus, hippocampus, and basal ganglia.

The midbrain is a small but important region of the brain that regulates motor control, sensory processing, and consciousness. It is essential in controlling visual and auditory reflexes that help to maintain and protect sensory organs. The midbrain also modulates pain perception and sensitivity. It is instrumental in maintaining arousal, by preventing drowsiness and promoting wakefulness in response to external stimuli.

The hindbrain consists of the cerebellum, pons, and medulla oblongata. It includes the upper section of the spinal cord and brainstem and is responsible for vital bodily functions like the coordination of motor functions, and the regulation of involuntary activities like heart rate and blood pressure. It is the relay station between the rest of the brain and both the spinal cord and cranial nerves by collecting signals from the body and integrating them to create a response to external stimuli.

An external view of the brain displays the cerebrum, which processes all conscious thoughts, memories, and actions. Split into two hemispheres by a deep fissure, the cerebrum allows for planning, thinking, reading, and communicating. Scientists are still unsure of the reason why the two hemispheres control opposite sides of the body.

The surface of the cerebrum and cerebellum is surrounded by a thick layer of gray matter called the cerebral cortex, which is responsible for most of the processing of information in the brain.

The Ever-Evolving Field of Neuroscience

The ever-expanding field of neuroscience has provided invaluable insight into the brain and nervous system, allowing for the significant improvement of human health. While physicians, scientists, and philosophers have been intrigued by the brain and its functions for thousands of years, recent decades have shown significant surges in the understanding of how the brain works. Stryker (2014) identifies major recent discoveries in the field of neuroscience, which include the following (*The evolution of neuroscience*, 2019, para 4):

- insight into the plasticity of the brain
- identifying defects in single genes that influence neurological disorders
- understanding the brain's reactions to social stimuli
- breakthroughs in Brain-Computer Interfaces (BCI)
- understanding how memories are stored and accessed
- developing implant therapies to treat neurological disorders

In the last five decades, neuroscience has produced the connectome, a breakthrough in brain-connectivity mapping (discussed in Chapter

5). Connectomics has allowed scientists to accurately map and track neural circuits at numerous scales from individual neurons to entire brain regions. In addition to this, the ability of scientists to access high-resolution images of processes in the brain has allowed them to understand the interplay between the brain and behavior. It is predicted that the next few decades will see a surge in the understanding of neural plasticity and malleability that will influence how scientists see brain development as influenced by genetics and environment. These advances in neuroscience will greatly enhance the understanding of various neurological disorders and potential therapeutic interventions.

The Ongoing Quest

Encouraging Further Exploration

The advent of advanced technology like high-powered microscopy and artificial intelligence (AI) has significantly amplified our understanding of the brain. The expanded capacity of computers to produce extensive outputs of information has provided neuroscientists with more information than ever before. Scientists are now able to examine the brain and various neurological disorders, illnesses, and trauma without relying on injuries or intrusive surgery. However, despite the vast and complex mapping of the brain's neural circuitry, scientists are still unable to fully read and understand this huge connectome.

Various experts suggest that AI will grow the field of neuroscience by allowing researchers and scientists to not only learn more about the brain and its cognitive abilities but also diagnose and treat neurological disorders. Besides the 85 billion neurons present in the brain, there are trillions of synapses between these neurons, each working together to create an intricate web of communication, one which scientists are striving to map and understand. These neurons and connections work in synergy with the body to allow for complex movements and cognitive processes. While working to map the brain's neural web, neuroscientists also aim to further understand "neurobiology at a cellular and molecular level and to generate new hypotheses addressing the molecular machinery that form, drive, and maintain the organization and function of the nervous system" (Koroshetz & Jakeman, 2023, para. 6). In other words, by understanding how the brain forms and develops at a microscopic level, scientists can gain better knowledge of how neural circuits process information.

The Importance of Brain Research for Humanity's Future

While the field of neuroscience has expanded in leaps and bounds over the last few decades, global mental health has seen a dramatic decline. Research shows that almost one billion people across the world suffer from a psychiatric disorder. Unfortunately, access to mental health facilities and treatment is not often available, especially in low-income settings. In addition, treatment is usually targeted at the symptoms of these disorders, not the underlying cause.

The future of neuroscience lies in the ability of scientists to diagnose neurological disorders before symptoms appear and treat them effectively. Neuro-technology also aims to enhance humans' cognitive abilities, as well as their ability to heal after major brain trauma and illness. As it stands, brain mapping has allowed neuroscientists to detect early signs of Alzheimer's disease and schizophrenia before symptoms appear.

Currently, BCIs are providing patients with debilitating neurological disorders the ability to perform tasks like moving limbs and perceiving sensory information. This is called "brain prosthetics." However, BCIs are moving beyond applications such as these and into education, gaming, and security. This is going to extend the field of BCIs beyond the medical and make it available to the general public. Further, advanced AI systems are being developed that aim to diagnose illnesses or diversions from normal brain functioning and track these ailments so that preventative treatment can be implemented before symptoms worsen.

The future of neuroscience is promising to revolutionize the understanding of the human brain and its underlying functions. Innovative technology and approaches to the science are poised to change how scientists diagnose, manage, and treat neurological and psychiatric disorders and trauma. Advances in the field offer a future of enhanced cognitive function, improved treatments for brain disorders, and the betterment of overall human health and well-being.

THANKS FOR READING

Dear reader,

Thank you for reading *A Map of the Human Brain: The Gross Anatomy of the Human Brain.*

If you enjoyed this book, please leave a review where you bought it. It helps more than most people think.

Don't forget your FREE book!

You will also be among the first to know of FREE review copies, discount offers, bonus content, and more.

Go to:

https://www.SFNonfictionBooks.com/Free-Book

Thanks again for your support.

AUTHOR RECOMMENDATIONS

Unlock Your Cognitive Power

Reinvigorate your mindset, because a vibrant mind creates a vibrant life.

Get it now.

www.SFNonfictionBooks.com/Active-Mind-Maintanance

Nourish Yourself for Life!

These are the balanced eating strategies you need, because longevity starts on your plate.

Get it now.

www.SFNonfictionBooks.com/Eat-Smart-For-Life

ABOUT SAM FURY

www.SamFury.com

Sam Fury has had a passion for survival, evasion, resistance, and escape (SERE) training since he was a young boy growing up in Australia.

This led him to years of training and career experience in related subjects, including martial arts, military training, and outdoor pursuits.

These days, he spends his time refining his skills and sharing what he learns via his books and blog.

amazon.com/stores/Sam-Fury/author/B00C8Z4U8S

facebook.com/SamFuryOfficial

instagram.com/samfuryofficial

youtube.com/@SamFuryOfficial

x.com/Samfuryoriginal

tiktok.com/@samfuryofficial

REFERENCES

https://web.stanford.edu/class/history13/earlysciencelab/body/brainpages/brain.html

https://theconversation.com/what-brain-regions-control-our-language-and-how-do-we-know-this-63318

https://bna.org.uk/about/about-neuroscience/

https://neuro.georgetown.edu/about-neuroscience

https://humanconnectome.org/about-ccf

https://medicalnewstoday.com/articles/313295

https://kenhub.com/en/library/anatomy/basal-ganglia

https://sitn.hms.harvard.edu/flash/2023/neuroplasticity-how-lost-skills-can-be-regained-after-injury-or-illness/

https://linkedin.com/pulse/intersection-ai-neuroscience-understanding-enhancing-human-balroop-zoxbc/

https://embryo.asu.edu/pages/neural-crest

https://teachmeanatomy.info/the-basics/embryology/central-nervous-system/

https://nbcnews.com/mach/science/three-myths-about-brain-deserve-die-n744956

https://my.clevelandclinic.org/health/body/23962-basal-ganglia

https://ncbi.nlm.nih.gov/books/NBK544297/

https://teachmeanatomy.info/back/nerves/spinal-cord/

https://memory.ucsf.edu/symptoms/behavior

https://nimh.nih.gov/health/topics/bipolar-disorder

https://betterhealth.vic.gov.au/health/conditionsandtreatments/brain#cerebrum-cerebral-cortex-and-brain-hemispheres

https://hopkinsmedicine.org/health/conditions-and-diseases/anatomy-of-the-brain

https://ninds.nih.gov/health-information/public-education/brain-basics/brain-basics-know-your-brain

https://ninds.nih.gov/health-information/public-education/brain-basics/brain-basics-life-and-death-neuron

https://ninds.nih.gov/health-information/public-education/brain-basics/brain-basics-understanding-sleep

https://startingblocks.gov.au/other-resources/factsheets/brain-development-in-children

https://simplypsychology.org/limbic-system.html

https://simplypsychology.org/temporal-lobe.html

https://sabinorecovery.com/rewiring-the-brain-after-trauma/

https://teachmeanatomy.info/neuroanatomy/structures/basal-ganglia/

https://nba.uth.tmc.edu/neuroscience/m/s1/chapter03.html

https://healthline.com/health/synaptic-pruning

https://hms.harvard.edu/news/new-field-neuroscience-aims-map-connections-brain

https://physio-pedia.com/Cerebellum

https://technologynetworks.com/neuroscience/articles/neuroimaging-techniques-and-what-a-brain-image-can-tell-us-363422

https://verywellhealth.com/what-are-glial-cells-and-what-do-they-do

https://ninds.nih.gov/news-events/directors-messages/all-directors-messages/looking-future-fundamental-neuroscience

https://ncbi.nlm.nih.gov/books/NBK557811/

https://psychcentral.com/health/what-part-of-the-brain-controls-speech

https://hopkinsmedicine.org/health/treatment-tests-and-therapies/rehabilitation-after-traumatic-brain-injury

https://healthline.com/health/neurons/

https://verywellmind.com/psychiatric-disorder-definition-425317

https://medicalnewstoday.com/articles/307076

https://britannica.com/science/ependymal-cell

https://news-medical.net/health/The-Anatomy-of-the-Human-Brain.aspx

https://healthline.com/health/diagnostics/10123-pet-scan

https://ncbi.nlm.nih.gov/books/NBK470353/

https://alz.org/alzheimers-dementia/what-is-alzheimers

https://who.int/news-room/questions-and-answers/item/mental-health-neurological-disorders

https://ncbi.nlm.nih.gov/books/NBK234146/

https://flo.health/pregnancy/pregnancy-health/fetal-development/fetal-brain-development

https://verywellmind.com/what-brain-plasticity-2794886

https://verywellmind.com/stages-of-prenatal-development-2795073

https://verywellmind.com/what-is-cognition-2794982

https://verywellmind.com/lesson-three-brain-and-behavior-2795291

https://verywellmind.com/what-is-phrenology-2795251

https://verywellmind.com/phineas-gage-279524

https://verywellmind.com/what-are-the-symptoms-of-schizophre
nia-2953120

https://doi.org/10.1523/JNEUROSCI.0744-19.2019

https://doi.org/10.1093/cercor/bhp120

https://doi.org/10.1038/526147a

https://doi.org/10.1016/B978-0-444-64150-2.00009-5

https://doi.org/10.3389/fncir.2020.00018

https://doi.org/10.1186/s12987-020-00230-3

https://doi.org/10.1111/apa.15810

https://doi.org/10.41392-023-01481-w

Printed in Great Britain
by Amazon

48537736R00059